A Collection of

Chin Folktales

Translated by Jessica Van Iangpar

Illustrated by Thinhnem Par Lian

Printed in the United States of America

Table of Contents

"This book contains a wonderful collection of classic Chin folktales. Jessica Van Iangpar has done a fabulous job of translating them into English—making them accessible to a new generation of readers. As a kindergartner in my class several years ago Jessica possessed an unparalleled zeal for life and strong work ethic. It is evident she has poured herself into this project and the final product is absolutely wonderful!"

Lindsey Mohamed
Kindergarten Teacher
Brimhall Elementary, MN

"It was my good fortune to meet Jessica and her family when she was in my second-grade class. Jessica was already displaying her writing talents at that young age and enjoyed sharing her Chin heritage with the class. This collection of folktales will give you insights not only into our shared humanity but into the history and values of the Chin people. Readers will be able to let their imaginations delight in Jessica's descriptions of characters and find similarities in folktales of other cultures. My hope is that children and parents will be enchanted with these stories and encouraged to share with others the magic of reading."

Lynn Thompson
2nd Grade Teacher (Retired)
Panther Lake Elementary
Kent, WA

"I had the privilege of being Jessica's fifth grade teacher in 2018. She was a wonderful student with a desire to learn, and an unquenchable thirst for knowledge. I recognized her ability to write with a mature style very quickly. I remember that her first "genius hour" project in my classroom was a Google Slide presentation about Myanmar. Jessica spoke, with confidence to her classmates, and presented a beautifully written and illustrated slide show titled, "Inside the Life of Myanmar (Burma)". I could tell how much she enjoyed sharing knowledge with others. She went on to research, write, and create more slide presentations that her peers always looked forward to hearing.

Even as a 5th grader, Jessica enjoyed sharing her culture with others. She had a gift then, and it continues to grow now. This endeavor to share stories that are such an important part of her culture with other children and their families shows a great maturity and love. Jessica's ability as a writer will continue to be a blessing to her and many families for years to come. I am extremely proud of Jessica and her hard work to make this project possible. It is with unwavering pride and confidence that I recommend this work of heart and art by Jessica Iangpar."

Shannon Betz
5th Grade ELA Teacher
Kitley Intermediate
Indianapolis, IN

"A Collection of Chin Folktales, replete with mermaids, dragons, fairies, exotic animals, damsels in distress, and valiant heroes, offers something for readers of all ages and interests. With a writing maturity that belies her age, Jessica Iangpar's voice rings true in her unique writing style, development of engaging characters, and colorful reminders of valuable life lessons. Iangpar's interpretations of ancient Chin folktales skillfully and colorfully relate tales of adventure, beauty, and virtue to an audience thirsty for cultural appreciation. Iangpar offers a fresh new perspective on classic Chin pieces, allowing past generations to connect with contemporary ones."

Rae Ann Woodrow
English/Language Arts Teacher (28 years)
Franklin Central Junior High School
Indianapolis, IN

"Whether we agree or not with any of the metaphors—melting pot, mosaic, salad bowl, kaleidoscope—in describing the US, it is undeniable that this vast country is made up of every part of the world. For a peaceful integration in this country, we need to respect and be interested in not just our own culture, but also those of our neighbors and our fellow people. This book is a vivid translation of the Chin folklores, full of intricate tales complemented by Jessica's precise attention to details. I believe her work will make a pivotal impact in not just the Chin community, but for anyone interested in different cultures."

Thlasui Tluangneh
Director
Christian Education & Literature Department
Chin Baptist Churches USA

Acknowledgement

Writing this book was rather challenging. I knew that it would take a while and that a few people would need to be involved in this project. It did take a couple of months to finally finish everything, but it was all thanks to the great help of the following individuals.

Firstly, I would like to thank God for the gift of writing instilled within me, and guiding me throughout the making of this book. Without God's help, I would never have been able to publish this book. I give my utmost thanks to God.

Next, I wish to thank my parents for cheering me on while I wrote this book. Your encouragement and enthusiasm really lifted my spirit, even when I thought it was all a futile attempt. Thank you to my mother, Tluang Cer Ṭial, for uplifting me from the sidelines and thank you to my father, Hrang Hlei, for giving me the idea to create this book and for supporting me the entire way as I wrote. You are both amazing, and I love you so much!

Thirdly, I am very grateful for my wonderful editor, Aunty Jane Ann (Jane Ann Nelson). Thank you so much for taking the time to look through my writings and editing all of my grammatical errors, while adding in meaningful suggestions and inspiring comments.

Also, I give my thanks to my brilliant illustrator, ka u Aa Hnem (Thinhnem Par Lian). Your illustrations are just superb, and I wouldn't have wanted any other person drawing for my book. Many children are not interested in reading a plain writing, but they prefer looking at illustrations in books. Your illustrations make this book more readable. I am very grateful that you agreed to become my illustrator.

Thank you so much to each and every one of my teachers who agreed to partake in this project. That includes Mrs. Mohammed, my amazing kindergarten teacher, Mrs. Thompson, my amazing second grade teacher, Mrs. Betz, my amazing fifth grade teacher, and Mrs. Woodrow, my amazing current Language Arts teacher. I am very delighted that you decided to endorse in my book!

Last but certainly not least, thank you to ka pa Rocung Pa (Saya Thlasui Tluangneh) for helping me publish this book. I could have written everything and all the illustrations could have been drawn, but it would have all been in vain if you had not helped us to publish it.

Thank you to everyone who has encouraged me to keep going: my friends, my teachers, and my family members. Without your encouragement and support, I would never have been able to finish this book. Thank you!

Editor's Preface

I met Jessica Van Iangpar a few days before her second birthday when she arrived in Minnesota after a 36-hour journey from Myanmar with her mother. She was alert and curious. Jessica, who had been learning her parents' Chin Language, immediately began experimenting with the cadences, rhythms, and sounds of English. Though she was not yet speaking English words, the sounds from her mouth "seemed" to be English.

In my weekly visits to her mother for practice in speaking English, both mother and daughter became my treasured friends. Jessica was very present, extremely curious, always asking, "What's that?" and "What's that?" She loved to learn new words! When the movie *Frozen* became popular, Jessica, a 6-year-old, not surprisingly quickly learned and belted out the lyrics of its songs—on pitch, too:

"Let It Go"
I don't care what they're going to say.
Let the storm rage on.
The cold never bothered me anyway.
It's time to see what I can do
To test the limits and break through.
No right, no wrong, no rules for me.
I'm free.
Let it go. Let it go.

When Jessica was 9, she made an important journey back to Myanmar to visit her extended family. Upon returning to the U.S., her father asked if she might write a little newsletter article to share her experiences with our church community. Jessica wrote an expressive four pages! She recounted "TRUE HORRORS" and "SUPER fun" and a visit to the King's Palace where she bought a souvenir: A book about

Burmese Folktales! I love traditional folktales! And the rest is, as they say, history.

So, it is not surprising that at the age of 12, Jessica has translated into English a collection of Chin Folktales. She loves mythology—whether Chinese, Japanese, Greek, or Norse—and wants to preserve and share the stories from her ancestral heritage with young Chin immigrants in the US as well as non-Chin speakers of all ages. Furthermore, she discovers delight in the fun exercise of finding the right English word to express the Chin idea.

While Jessica—and often her readers of these Chin folktales—might wish that young girls (and princesses) might have more agency in making decisions about their lives, or that disputes were not solved with violence and killing, or that strangers were not so often treated as suspect, she—and we—appreciate the tales for what they are: a rich reflection of the Chin culture.

Through the years when asked what her favorite school subject is, Jessica has often answered, "language arts." And to the question of what she wants to become, she responds, "a writer." With this publication, Jessica is "test[ing] the limits and break[ing] through." She is "see[ing] what [she] can do." And she has indeed become a writer!

Jane Ann Nelson
Director of Library Services Emerita
Augsburg University
Minneapolis, MN

Foreword

Jessica was born in Mandalay, Myanmar, while I was at Princeton for my further study. She and her mom (my wife) arrived in the US when I was pursuing a doctoral degree at Luther Seminary, St. Paul, MN. Jessica and I met in person for the first time when she turned two years old. I noticed early on that she has the passion and gift of writing, and, thus, I have always encouraged her to focus on her passion. I pray that she will be able to pursue her dream to become an accomplished author in the future.

The origin of this little book began when Jessica and I stumbled across a YouTube channel in which classic Chin folktales were told. I encouraged her to translate these classic Chin folktales into English, so that many Chin younger generations—who are now in a variety of countries in Australia, Europe and North America—would be able to read them in the language they are familiar with and to connect with their own roots. Without much thinking, she agreed to embark on this rather challenging project.

There are at least three reasons why I encouraged my daughter to translate the Chin folktales into English. First, since she is interested in classic literature, I want her to engage and get acquainted with the Chin folktales as a classic literature. Next, many Chin younger generations who are in Europe, North America and other developed countries tend to forget their social and cultural roots—who they are and where their parents and grandparents came from. This little book will be a helpful resource for them to understand part of the Chin social and cultural backgrounds. Third, since no one has ever translated the Chin folktales into English before, I encouraged Jessica to translate them so that English-speaking audiences will have a chance to read the classic tales of the Chin people. By reading this book, the readers will also learn more about the Chin people and their culture, and they will realize many similarities in folktales of other cultures around the world.

My wife and I are very proud of Jessica for her courage to embark on this rather challenging project to translate these classic Chin folktales into English. We are especially grateful to God for instilling the gift of writing in her heart. We hope and pray that the readers will discover different genres and meanings embedded in these Chin folktales.

Hrang Hlei (Rev. Dr.)
Pastor
Indiana Chin Baptist Church
Indianapolis, IN

Introduction

The tales in this book are all Chin folktales, yes, but many readers may notice that they share many similar elements and plots with other classic tales from all around the world. Pretty much all of these stories are deprived from other tales foreign to Myanmar.

For instance, the tale of *Zawl Tling and Ngan Bawm*, one of the most popular Chin folktales, is very much like the beloved tale of *Romeo and Juliet* by William Shakespeare. Two youths who are deeply in love with each other are forbidden to be together, due to their families' different social classes and rivalry with each other.

The tale of *Man Vang and Man Bo* was most likely introduced to the Chin people by the Burmese. *The Big Tortoise* is a Burmese tale almost identical to *Man Vang and Man Bo.* There are only a few changes that were most likely put in to make more sense to the Chin people.

The collected stories in this book are told mostly in the Hakha region of Chin State. They are told in different regions as well, but these regions have altered versions of the tales so they fit their region.

There are countless versions of each story so it was slightly difficult to choose one reliable source. In the end, I used two sources to write the tales; one with a plot I would follow, and the other with names I would use. Before, *Man Vang and Man Bo* was *Than Cer and Man Bo*. Than Cer's Story was *Man Vang's Story.*

Because there are so many versions, people who are familiar with some of the tales may read this and think, 'this isn't right,' or, 'I was told this happened instead.' I wouldn't exactly call this book an adaptation of the original stories, because I only changed a few minor details. They are the original stories.

These folktales have become more and more ancient and forgotten as the years go by, especially with the Chin younger generations. It's not a surprise that most Chin children living in the U.S. have picked up on using English much more than their mother tongue. Many children have forgotten how to speak it completely.

I created this book because I wanted the younger generation of Chin people to learn more about and feel closer to their heritage. However, I can't promise that everybody will share the same connection as I do. Even so, I think it's good for the younger generations, both Chin and non-Chin, to read these kinds of folktales, as it increases their knowledge of the outside world.

Myanmar is a country that many foreigners have no idea exists. Chin State, being a small region in the northwest of Myanmar, is even more unknown. Nobody has ever translated these Chin folktales into English before and compiled them into a book. Especially not a twelve-year-old girl. This allows the majority of the world's population to go on living without a clue of Chin State and its culture.

To be completely honest, the idea of making this book was entirely spontaneous. I enjoyed retelling tales and lore in my journals whenever I was feeling bored. My father had found a Chin YouTube channel that told classic folktales, and he showed me one of the stories. It was the story of *Ngun Nu and Her Sister*.

I listened to it, and retold the story on a writing website. Following that, I told my parents about it and after reading my retelling of the tale, my father suggested I create an actual book filled with Chin folktales. It would be a great opportunity to display my writing and a great opportunity for others to learn more about the Chin culture. It didn't take me long to agree to it.

I cannot guarantee that this book will be perfect and that the readers will enjoy it; there are flaws in this book. Nonetheless, I hope that this book will be a helpful resource for the readers, and it will help them to expand their knowledge of the Chin people and their culture.

The Little Frog

The Little Frog is sort of like the Chin version of The Frog Prince. Of course, there are some major differences, but it shares vital fundamentals. Utlakte, or 'little frog,' is exactly what its name says he is: a little frog. He soon unexpectedly wishes for one of the king's daughters. The king makes an impossible bargain with Utlakte but to everybody's surprise, Utlakte manages to complete the king's task. When all of her older sisters refused the little frog, the youngest of the princesses steps up and marries Utlakte to save her father. Life is not the most luxurious with Utlakte but soon, the princess grows fond of Utlakte. After secretly testing her faith a few times, Utlakte transforms into a handsome young man and life is perfect for the couple.

There once was a widow who had a son. Her son wasn't like the rest of the humans. In fact, he wasn't a human at all! He was a little frog. The widow had named him Utlakte, which means 'little frog'. He was overall a polite, nice little frog who didn't get into mischief. Although he was just a little frog, Utlakte was very intelligent. The widow and her son lived together for many peaceful years in a tiny cottage.

Now, in their area, lived a wealthy king. The king had five stunning daughters who all attracted many men from across the world. However, the king was very protective of them and didn't permit them to be married to any man who he thought would cause them sorrow.

One day, Utlakte went up to his mother and spontaneously asked if she could go to the king's palace and ask for one of his daughters' hands in marriage. The old widow refused and called him crazy to think that the king would ever agree.

"Of course not! Why would you ever ask me that? If I were to do as you wished, we'd become the laughing stock of the village. The king would be furious, and he'd think that we disrespect him," she explained. However, Utlakte nagged her every day until she finally gave in. Reluctantly, the old widow traveled to the palace, for she loved her son so much.

She entered the palace and eventually was given the consent to meet with the king. "Alright, explain what you have to ask of me," the king said. Anxiously, the old widow explained everything to the king. "Your majesty, my son has been very much infatuated and in love with your daughters. He asks me every single day to come to you and ask for one of your daughter's hands in marriage." The old widow shivered timidly as the king's formerly calm expression converted to a disgruntled one.

After she finished, the king asked the old widow what her son's name was. She told him that Utlakte was her son's name. The king was infuriated. 'How dare a little frog even *think* of asking for one of my daughters?' he thought to himself. He was ready to shout at the old widow when he realized that it wouldn't be good for his reputation if he punished a person because of a mere marriage proposal. So, he decided to make Utlakte do the impossible in order to punish him.

"Well, if your son really loves my daughters that much, he must make every single pavement and road surrounding my palace shine strikingly by polishing it, *by tonight*," the king ordered. The widow was about to call the deal off and simply go back home, ready to break the news to Utlakte, when the king continued.

"If he doesn't do this, I will have both of you executed for disrespecting me." There was no way out of it. The old widow ran back home, sobbing the entire way. "Utlakte, oh Utlakte! You have really done it now! We will both die tomorrow! I kept on telling you that it wasn't possible, but you kept on nagging and now we're going to die!" the widow wept in despair.

Utlakte, not understanding what his mother meant, questioned her. "What do you mean? What did the king say?" he demanded. The old widow didn't want to tell him at first, but she eventually let it out. "The king is going to kill us if you do not polish all the pavements and roads around his house so that they shine by tonight. If you somehow miraculously manage to complete this, the king will give you one of his daughters."

That night, Utlakte woke his old mother up and said, "Come, Mother. We have to head to the palace so we can carry out the king's order." The old widow shook her head. "No, you can never do it. Just let us die," she said grievously. So, Utlakte went by himself. The old widow, anxious to see whatever might happen to her son, eventually followed.

When the king woke up early the next morning, he looked out of his window, expecting to see the same old pavement and streets surrounding his palace. However, when he looked closer, he saw that they were all thoroughly polished to the point where they shone and glimmered. The king was astonished, as were his subjects.

He called to his five daughters and announced that one of them would have to marry Utlakte. "Me? Marry a frog? You must be teasing, Father," the oldest one replied in a discourteous tone. "Disgusting! Why would I marry a frog?" exclaimed the second daughter, obviously repulsed. "I'm sorry, Father. I don't want to. I'd rather die than marry a frog," said the third daughter slightly more civilly.

"Never! I don't care if you die, Father. I refuse to marry that creature!" the fourth daughter exclaimed in a livid tone. The king was heartbroken. "If you don't agree to marry him, they have the right to kill me!" he pleaded with his daughters. He turned to his youngest daughter and dropped to his knees, frantically pleading, asking her to marry Utlakte.

The youngest daughter was the kindest. She couldn't bear to see her father so upset. "For you, Father, I will marry the little frog. I could not endure if you were to be killed because of me," she said. The king embraced his daughter and thanked her gratefully.

So, she took off from the palace in search of Utlakte's house. On her way, she picked up a handful of worms and other crawly, unsettling little insects, thinking Utlakte would like to eat them. Eventually, she found the house and entered.

Utlakte had been inside an earthen jar at the moment. He hopped out of the jar and the princess handed him all the insects she had collected. Utlakte found all of it rather kind and the food was delectable. After consuming it, Utlakte and the princess were married.

Although the princess wasn't fond of Utlakte at first, the couple soon became close and not long after, the princess fell in love. Every day, Utlakte's mother and the princess went out to the fields to work. Each time, the princess would pick up the foods that Utlakte liked: worms and other small bugs. The princess always fed them to him.

One day, the princess went out to the field by herself. As she stood on a porch (in Chin, *Tlaitlan*), she spotted a very handsome young man. The man was attractive and aristocratic-looking. He was wearing fine robes, specifically that of a prince's garments.

"I wish that young man would come over here to chat with me," she whispered to herself. Almost as if the young man had heard her wish, he strolled over to her. "Excuse me, miss, but aren't you a princess?" he asked graciously. The princess nodded.

"Then how come you're not in a palace with all your beautiful riches and silks? Why are you here, busily working in the fields like a peasant?" The princess explained everything to him. "You see, I am the wife of a little frog named, Utlakte."

The young man held his hand out to her. "Come with me, princess. You can marry me and leave this wretched life. We can run away together and your Utlakte will not be able to find us," he offered. To this, the princess stood up, visibly furious with him.

"How dare you suggest such a thing? Never. Go away and leave us alone!" she rejected him with a fiery tone. The princess was quite scandalized and outraged. Obediently, the young man went away. After a while, the princess returned home, making sure to bring her collection of "food" for Utlakte. Like always, Utlakte was inside his little earthen jar when she arrived. The princess fed him the food and once more, Utlakte was contented.

On another occasion, both the princess and her mother-in-law went out into the fields to do some work again. Near evening, Utlakte hopped out of his little earthen jar and went outside. When he did, he slipped and accidentally fell inside a ditch that people used as a toilet. He couldn't get out and it was so dirty and sickening inside.

The princess and the old widow returned home near nightfall, but when they checked inside the little earthen jar, Utlakte wasn't there. They searched around some more until finally the princess heard his desperate cries from the ditch. She darted to it, and although it was tremendously revolting, she took a lengthy stick and fished Utlakte out. The princess bathed him and fed him the bugs she had collected in the fields.

Months passed by and the family began to run out of food to eat. "I will journey to my home and ask my Father to provide us with food," the princess volunteered. During her trip, Utlakte had transformed into a handsome young man and turned their house into a magnificent, enchanting, palace-like estate. The princess returned with her entire family and her father's soldiers. They had helped her carry the foods.

When they reached the little town where she had lived with Utlakte, she looked around for their house but couldn't find it. The princess was greatly distressed until her mother-in-law called to her and her family, inviting them into the glorious house.

Before doing anything else, the princess darted towards Utlakte's earthen jar. She was planning to surprise him with the worms and other bugs she had collected during her journey. Stealthily, she peeked inside of the jar, but nothing was inside.

Perplexed, she asked the widow where Utlakte was. "Oh, he's outside talking with your Father, dear," she answered. The princess sprinted outside and gasped when she saw Utlakte. He was the handsome, prince-like young man she had met in the field months before.

She was very thrilled and praised God. "God has blessed me because I have obeyed my father," she exclaimed. He older sisters who had refused to marry Utlakte in the beginning, were very envious of her. They dressed themselves in pretty clothes and made sure to put on dazzling makeup in hopes that Utlakte would notice and fall in love with them.

However, to their disappointment, he didn't even glance at them. The princess was all he loved. Soon, the princess gave birth to a son for Utlakte and they became the cheeriest, most wealthy and loving family in their village and all the neighboring lands.

The Story of Nga Tai (Mermaid)

This tale tells the story of how mermaids in Chin State came to be. The beautiful Nga Tai and her elderly mother lived tranquilly in their little village for a long time. One year, their years of peace came to an end when a great flood caused the village to migrate from mountain to mountain. To appease the raging waves, the villagers sacrificed Nga Tai against her and her mother's will. However, due to her mother's great love, Nga Tai transformed into a beautiful mermaid!

Once upon a time, in a remote village in the Chin hills, there lived a poor old widow. She had one beautiful daughter by the name of Nga Tai. Nga Tai was so beautiful that whoever laid eyes on her was immediately enchanted. Her body structure was perfect and her face always looked attractive. Her eyes always twinkled with kindness, and it greatly resembled a glorious new dawn.

Nga Tai's long, silky hair was as black as a raven's feather and it sagged down gracefully when she walked around.

It wasn't only her external beauty that pleased people; her personality was extremely likeable as well. Nga Tai respected everybody and spoke in a sweet, gentle tone, never once raising her voice. Everybody always complimented Nga Tai on her amazing voice. She truly had a wonderful gift. Her mother was, of course, very proud of her.

One year, the heavens suddenly drenched the village. The rain was hard, vicious, and unforgiving. The villagers didn't think much of it at first, believing it would come to a stopping point soon. However, the rain didn't cease to pour down. It kept on raining and raining, to the point where it was flooding their houses and fields. The villagers quickly evacuated and tried to search for a haven.

They climbed several hills to escape the flooding but the water always caught up with them. Over and over again, the villagers ran to another hill but the water always followed. Those who couldn't make it were swept into the water and drowned. Finally, they reached the highest hill they could find. The furious water crept up towards them and swallowed all their animals, plants, and crops.

"How could this happen?" the villagers asked one another. "How do we stop this?" As they questioned each other, the water suddenly began to whisper. "Tai, Tai, Tai..." it said. The villagers stopped bickering and listened. "Tai, Tai, Tai..." the water repeated. The villagers turned to face Nga Tai and her mother. "The water must want Nga Tai," was their conclusion.

So, they plucked a strand of her hair and threw it in the raging waters. As soon as they did this, the water level rapidly lowered. "Tai," it whispered. For a short while, things seemed to be getting better but very soon, the water began to rise once more. "Tai, Tai, Tai..." The villagers then took Nga Tai's cloak and threw it in the water. Again, the water level rapidly lowered. "Tai," it whispered. Just when things began to brighten once more, the water began to rise for the second time, murmuring Nga Tai's name.

The villagers dropped her garments, her strands of hair, her jewelry, and everything else they could. However, the water never seemed to be pleased. It always rose back up. Now the villagers were crestfallen. They didn't know what to do. Of course, they could keep on giving Nga Tai's belongings to the water, but they realized that the outcome was going to be the same.

In the end, the villagers all agreed that instead of all of their lives being taken, it was better to sacrifice one person. They chose Nga Tai as the person who should die, for the water had been murmuring her name in the first place. They tried to seize her but the old widow blocked their way.

"No! This heavy rain was not my daughter's fault. So, why do any of you think it is okay to sacrifice my beloved Nga Tai?" she protested firmly. Despite her protests, the people pushed through and dragged poor Nga Tai out of her mother's arms.

Nga Tai screamed and cried out in fear of being engulfed by the water and drowned. But her pleas and cries fell on the villagers' deaf ears. They threw her in the water, and slowly, she sunk deeper and deeper until she was no longer in sight. The poor old widow dropped to her knees and sobbed.

"Oh, my treasured child, Nga Tai, I did not want to give you up... Please don't die; please turn into a mermaid (in Chin, *Nga Tai*) instead," she begged. The water rapidly began to sink back to its normal state. Although the villagers did not know it, Nga Tai had, in fact, turned into a mermaid, just as her mother had wished. That is why, according to Chin folklore, mermaids appear to have human features in their upper body.

This made the old widow sick from heartache. She was so lonely and grief-stricken. The widow continually journeyed around hills and mountains in search of her daughter to no avail. Out of sheer loneliness, the old widow would look for high mountains so she could weave. Finally, the old widow found a scenic mountain that proved to pacify her.

So, the old widow climbed that mountain and began to weave away. The widow stretched her loom to a mountain called *Zinghmuh Tlang* (God-seeing mountain). When Nga Tai saw her lonely mother's weaving, she transformed into a human and visited her. However, since she was already a mermaid, she could not keep her human form for long. So, Nga Tai miserably transformed back into a mermaid. Nonetheless, the widow was so blissful to see her daughter again. Even after the old widow had passed away, Nga Tai would still visit the mountain where her mother had woven. People would see her walking up the mountain, and they were bewildered by her form.

Her upper body was that of a woman but her lower half was a fish's body! Due to this, the people named the mountain, *"Nga Tai Nu Tlang,"* or in English, "Mermaid Mountain. The mountain is still known today as Nga Tai Nu Tlang. It is located near the town of Thantlang in Chin State, Myanmar. Legend has it that the widow's loom stayed on the mountain for many generations.

The Lasi (Fairy) Queen

*The Lasi Queen tells the legend of a peculiar love story
between a human and a fairy. A young man, craving
adventure and success, decides to assist a Burmese king by
bringing him the little golden bird he wished to hear sing.
The little golden bird belonged to a refined Lasi Queen, who
lived deep in the woods. With the help of a little Lasi, the
young man manages to steal two of the Lasi Queen's most
prized possessions. In the process, however, both the young
man and the queen fall in love. Things suddenly go south for
the young man and he is treated unfairly, but very soon, the
Lasi Queen journeys to the human kingdom and changes the
young man's life for the better.*

Long ago, there lived a Lasi queen. The queen was a beautiful individual, with luscious golden hair and smooth, fair skin. All Lasi were known to be very pretty creatures, but the queen surpassed the limit. She was even more beautiful than the average Lasi.

She lived in a very deep, thick, and cryptic forest. Her home lay beyond the ninth layer of the deep forest. The queen had one thousand brave soldiers who guarded her night and day with great precision. She had a little golden bird and a golden box. Her little golden bird had a truly unique voice, and it was a marvelous singer.

In her forest kingdom, there were two rivers: one that gave a person eternal youth and beauty, and one that made a person elderly. During her time, there also lived a Burmese king who was very wealthy and powerful. The Burmese king planted all sorts of beautiful flowers and fruits around his grand palace. His palace was an extremely luxurious and astounding place. He was surrounded by his soldiers, his servants, and their families.

One day, the Lasi queen's little golden bird flew to a nearby area of the Burmese king's palace. The little bird was immediately attracted by the colorful flowers, and vibrant plants and fruits. 'How wonderful it would be if my queen could rule over such a wonderous place such as this one!' thought the little bird.

Then, the little golden bird began to sing out of bliss. The king's soldiers who had been patrolling the area heard the melodious voice of the little bird. They thought to themselves, 'what an amazing voice,' and all quieted down to listen to it.

It was such a good voice that they rushed back to the palace and informed their king. The king immediately wanted to hear the voice of the little bird. "Capture the bird and bring it to me," he ordered them.

The soldiers found the little bird very quickly, but they could not capture it. It always flew away before they were about to capture it. Again, and again they attempted to catch it but in vain. Finally, they gave up and returned to their king. "It was a golden bird, your highness. We tried many times to catch it but we never could," they explained.

"Do not stop until you find and catch the bird!" he demanded. So, the unfortunate soldiers went out to search for the little golden bird once more. They searched and searched for the bird until they finally caught sight of it. However, it disappeared into a cliff where the Lasi kingdom was situated. The soldiers could no longer follow it.

When the king learned that he could not listen to the bird, he was very upset to the point where he would not eat. Soon, the king announced to his kingdom that whoever could capture the little golden bird will inherit his daughter and his kingdom.

Near his kingdom, there was a village in which three brothers lived. The three brothers enjoyed hunting activities such as laying bird traps, (in Chin, *va rap chiah*) log traps, (in Chin, *Mangkhawng*) and shooting wild animals. The brothers were living a very poor life but they always managed to find enough food because of their hard work.

One day, the three brothers were out in the forest, laying log traps as usual. Nothing too exciting was happening. But suddenly, the youngest brother gasped and cried out in surprise, for in his log trap, there was a little Lasi!

The frightened little creature struggled in her trap and tried desperately to escape. The youngest brother cautiously grabbed the Lasi and held her tightly so that she would not run away. "Let me go!" shrieked the Lasi frantically.

"No, I will not let you go," replied the youngest brother, still maintaining his firm grip on her. She struggled some more and cried out to let her go, but every time, the youngest brother refused to grant her wish.

Finally, in a desperate attempt to escape, the Lasi asked the youngest brother, "What do you want? I will do whatever you want." The youngest brother did not hesitate one minute to answer. "The Burmese king has sent out a proclamation that whoever can capture and bring him a little golden bird will inherit his daughter and his entire kingdom. I would like to capture that bird, so you must help me."

The little Lasi gave the youngest brother three things: First, she reached in her pocket and pulled out a leather blanket embroidered with plaid designs. Second, the Lasi gave him a comb. Finally, she gave him an egg.

"Follow this trail and you will eventually find a great white horse tied up at the entrance to a village. This horse is not tame yet, so it is very wild and dangerous. You will cover his back with the blanket and hold onto his muzzle. This will calm him down. You will ride on the horse and he will bring you to the place where the little golden bird is. Before you reach the ninth layer of the forest, you will encounter three elderly women. They will give you instructions and you are to listen carefully to them. Make sure to remember all their instructions.

"The little golden bird belongs to the Lasi queen. She lives beyond the ninth layer of the forest. It is her custom to stay in a peaceful slumber for one month and stay awake for the next month. It is at this time that the Lasi queen is sleeping for a month, making it the best time to take her bird. The little golden bird rests above the queen's head. You will pluck a strand of the queen's golden hair and tie it around the bird's beak. Only then will the little bird be silenced and you can escape without being heard."

After she finished the instructions, the youngest brother asked, "What am I to do with the comb and the egg you gave me?"

"If all goes well and you can silence the bird, you will put it in a golden box and run away as fast as you can. However, if the queen's soldiers chase after you, you will throw the comb at them and witness wonderous things. If this fails and they still chase after you, you will throw the egg at them."

So, the youngest brother thanked the little Lasi and set her free. He went back to his brothers and told them that he would go on a journey and wouldn't return for a while. "Will you bring our horse with you?" inquired his older brothers.

"No, I will find a horse by myself," the youngest brother answered.

With that, he set off for his journey. Like the little Lasi had told him, the youngest brother followed the trail and arrived at a village. There was, as the little Lasi had told him, a great white horse tied up at the entrance.

The youngest brother covered the white horse's back with the plaid leather blanket and held onto his muzzle. The horse calmed down and they galloped away from the village. After riding for a while, the youngest brother and his horse reached the third layer of the forest.

In the third layer of the forest, the youngest brother spotted a seventy-year-old woman. "My grandson, where are you going?" she said in a gentle voice. "I am going to capture a little golden bird," he replied. "Come to my house to eat some food before you go," offered the old woman. The youngest brother followed the old woman to her house and enjoyed the delicious food she made him.

When he finished eating, the old woman told him that the Lasi queen had a river that gave a person eternal youth and beauty. "When you have captured the little bird, please bring me a bottle of water from that river," she requested. "Of course!" the youngest brother exclaimed and continued on with his journey.

In the sixth layer of the forest, the youngest brother spotted a ninety-year-old woman. "My grandson, where are you going?" she said in a gentle voice. "I am going to capture a little golden bird," he replied. "Come to my house to eat some food before you go," offered the old woman. The youngest brother followed the old woman to her house and enjoyed the delicious food she made him.

"My grandson, I am old now. When you have captured the little bird, please bring me two bottles of water from the river of youth and beauty," she requested. "Of course!" he exclaimed and continued on with his journey.

In the eighth layer of the forest, the youngest brother spotted a very old woman, a woman over the age of one hundred. "My grandson, where are you going?" she said in a gentle voice. "I am going to capture a little golden bird," he replied. "Come to my house to eat some food before you go," offered the old woman. The youngest brother followed the old woman to her house and enjoyed the delicious food she made him.

"My grandson, I am very old now. When you have captured the little bird, please bring me three bottles of water from the river of youth and beauty," she requested. "Of course!" he exclaimed and continued on with his journey.

Finally, he arrived beyond the ninth layer of the forest. The youngest brother saw thousands of soldiers guarding the queen's house but they were all sound asleep. Even the large elephants guarding with the soldiers were asleep.

Carefully, the youngest brother passed all the guards and entered the home of the Lasi queen. She was sleeping peacefully in her bed. The Lasi queen was so beautiful that the youngest brother fell into a slight trance when he saw her. He stood motionless for a while, admiring the queen's exquisite beauty.

When he fell out of the trance, the youngest brother caught sight of the little golden bird above the queen's head. He plucked a strand of the queen's gorgeous golden hair and tied it around the bird's beak, as the little Lasi had instructed. The youngest brother put the little bird inside the golden box. As he was about to head out the door, he suddenly could not stand the thought of leaving behind such a beautiful creature.

'I will stay a little bit to rub her lips,' he thought to himself. The youngest brother went back and caressed her face. However, when he began to rub her lips, the Lasi queen opened her eyes, revealing a brilliant twinkle. She had awoken!

The youngest brother immediately dashed out the door with the little golden bird and galloped away on his white horse. He stopped by the river of youth and beauty and collected some water in six bottles to bring back to the elderly women.

Back at the Lasi queen's house, the queen, who was very shocked and angry, screamed. "Humans have been in my kingdom! A young man just broke into my home! Chase after him!" she ordered her soldiers.

The Lasi soldiers instantly began to chase after the young man. Just as they were catching up to him, the youngest brother pulled out his egg and threw it at them. The egg cracked and without warning, a great, vast ocean separated him and Lasi soldiers.

However, this ocean would not stop the soldiers. Using their wings, they flew across the ocean and continued to chase after him. Again, when they were catching up to him, the youngest brother threw the comb at them. The comb turned into a huge, thick, and thorny bush.

The Lasi soldiers, being little people, got stuck attempting to squeeze through the thorny bush. As they struggled, the youngest brother was already far away from them. Eventually, the soldiers managed to make it out of the bush and continued to chase after him.

For a third time, as they were catching up to him, the youngest brother threw the leather blanket at them. The blanket suddenly transformed into a desert! The desert was so hot that the Lasi soldiers could no longer see him.

The soldiers finally gave up and returned to their kingdom. Their queen was still upset with the whole incident. "Not only did this man set foot in my kingdom and my home, but he also managed to steal my little golden bird and my golden box. This is no ordinary human. We must find him," she decided.

On his way back, the youngest brother visited the three old women and gave them the water from the river of youth and beauty as they had requested. All three women drank the water at the exact same time.

The youngest brother was astonished when the women turned into the little Lasi that he had trapped in his log trap! He stared at her some more. "You look just like the little Lasi I had trapped in my log trap," he told her.

"That is because I am. The three old women were all just me. I am very glad that you did exactly everything I told you to do," she smiled. "Thank you for all your help," said the youngest brother. "I will go home now."

"Make sure to be careful on the way home. You could get into danger," the little Lasi reminded him. "What kind of danger?"

"Nothing else will cause you harm, except your two older brothers," the little Lasi replied gravely. With this, the little Lasi bid him farewell and flittered away. Confused, the youngest brother headed back home.

When he arrived home, he told his brothers all about his adventure. The three brothers were very joyful. However, little did the youngest brother know that his older brothers were jealous of him. He would marry the king's daughter and inherit his entire kingdom!

That night, the two older brothers tied their younger brother up in ropes and took the little golden bird and the golden box. The next morning, their younger brother could not get up or move, for he was tied up.

"My brothers, if I receive something good, it means we all do!" he tried to reason with them. "We will all live in the king's palace!"

"No, it shouldn't be! The youngest in the family should not earn the right to be the ruler!" his brothers argued. "We will be the ones to marry the king's daughter and inherit his kingdom. Don't worry, we will make you chief of the soldiers," they said.

So, the older brothers took the golden bird and box and presented it to the king. The king was ecstatic. "How did you manage to capture it?" he asked them admiringly. The older brothers, not knowing how their younger brother captured the bird, did not know what to reply with.

"Well, make the bird sing," ordered the king. The older brothers tried to make the golden bird sing in its melodious voice, but since its beak was tied up in the Lasi queen's hair, it remained silent. Nobody knew how to remove the strand of hair, as it was magic. The king made the older brothers remove the strand of hair but to no prevail.

The king called to his royal advisor. "Why is this happening?" he asked. The royal advisor answered, "It is tied up by a golden strand of hair. Nobody in all of the Chin hills has golden hair, so whoever this hair belongs to must not be an ordinary person."

The royal advisor continued. "My king, I have heard of legends about a Lasi queen who lives beyond the ninth layer of the thickest forest. Not only is she extremely beautiful and graceful, people say she has amazing golden hair. According to the stories, this queen owns a little golden bird and a golden box."

After hearing this, the king asked the two brothers if they had any other siblings. "My king, we have one younger brother. But he is not even good for taking care of the house."

"Even though you cannot remove the strand of hair from the bird's beak, I am still grateful you brought it to me. So, as I promised, I will give my daughter and the king's title to the oldest brother. The younger brother, you will be crown prince. Bring your youngest brother. Poor thing. I will at least make him chief of the soldiers," said the fair king.

The brothers were extremely happy and they called their youngest brother. He went to the palace and told the king everything about his adventure. "I cannot remove the strand of hair from the bird's beak, though," he admitted to the king.

"Please make my oldest brother the king and arrange a wedding for him and your daughter, like you promised. Also, please make my older brother the crown prince. Then, I will think up of a way to remove the strand of hair from the bird's beak."

Meanwhile, the Lasi queen was very sorrowful and lonely. She missed her little golden bird so much. The image of the young man's handsome face lingered in her mind and struck her heart. She no longer knew what to think.

In the end, the Lasi queen made up her mind. She told her soldiers that they would all go to the human kingdom. The queen and her soldiers ventured out of the forest and on their way, they passed the third layer of the forest.

They came across the little Lasi that had helped the youngest brother with his quest. The Lasi queen questioned the little Lasi about the young man. The little Lasi told the queen all the the young man had done. So, the queen and her soldiers continued their journey to the human kingdom.

Soon, they arrived at the Burmese king's palace. The Lasi queen was so exceedingly beautiful that the humans all either fell in a trance or fainted when they saw her. Her beauty was so radiant that it showered light on the people's eyes.

All three brothers were standing in a line with the king. The king, who had fallen into a trance, snapped back to consciousness. "My lady, what is your purpose?" he asked respectfully. "I have come to retrieve my little golden bird, my golden box, and the young man who stepped foot on my kingdom," she replied.

"I'm very sorry, my lady, but I love the little golden bird very much. I cannot give it back to you. But I will certainly give you the young man you are looking for. Who is it?" said the king.

"The young man who stole my bird and box is the young man I am looking for," said the Lasi queen. The king turned to the brothers. "These three brothers are the young men who took it from you. Choose whichever brother you want."

The Lasi queen looked at the eldest and smiled. "This is not the one," she said. Then, she looked at the middle brother and smiled once more. "This is not the one, either," she said. Finally, the Lasi queen looked at the youngest brother and smiled warmly. The youngest brother smiled with her. "*This* is the one who stole my bird," she said.

"This man is also the one who can remove the strand of my hair from my bird's beak," she announced, turning to the king. So, the youngest brother touched the bird's beak and the strand of golden hair began to remove itself. It magically attached itself back onto the queen's head.

All the people who had witnessed it were very amazed. She turned to the king. "Let the oldest brother marry your daughter. Keep your promise with the middle brother, as well.

But the youngest brother will marry me and I will take him back to my kingdom."

"Alright, but please allow me to have your little golden bird," the king pleaded. The Lasi queen shook her head. "I'm very sorry, but you cannot have my golden bird. Without my little bird, I cannot live," she replied gently.

Sadly, the king agreed. Very soon, the king's daughter and the oldest brother were married. After staying in the human kingdom for a while, the Lasi queen decided it was time to go back to her own kingdom.

"It is not possible for us to always be in the human kingdom. I am a Lasi and you are all humans. We cannot live in peace together. My husband, my soldiers, and I shall return to my kingdom," she explained. So, they returned to the Lasi kingdom and lived happily ever after.

Heaven's Colt (Vancung Rangtum)

Vancung Rangtum is a tale of bravery and adventure. A young man who had nothing better to do than set traps for animals, finds himself on a near-impossible journey to free a princess from the clutches of a terrifying dragon. It would be impossible to defeat the dragon by himself, but due to the help of three mystic creatures, he befriends a great colt with a bird's wings. With the colt's assistance, the young man frees the princess, slays the dragon, and lives a life of peace and prosperity.

Once, a long time ago, there lived an elderly widow and her son. Her son was a rather handsome, healthy and active young man who showed much interest in hunting. Despite his many good features, the young man wasted much of his time setting bird and log traps (Log traps are used for hunting small animals in the forest).

Their village was ruled by a highly respected king who had one beautiful daughter. The king wanted his daughter to marry a hardworking, faithful, and handsome young man. The villagers were always buzzing to each other about who would one day marry the princess.

Beyond the king's palace there was a very high cliff. There was a deep and dangerous cave in the cliff. Nobody dared to go in the cave, for in it, there was an enormous, three-headed dragon (In Chin mythology, these are called *rul chuang ngei*).

Each year, the dragon would demand one human from the village to feast on in its cave. So, the villagers built a sacrificial stage (In Chin, *thawinak theng*) to offer the human body to the beast. The dragon would fly out of its cave and devour the human.

It was very upsetting to the villagers but it allowed them to live in peace. One tragic year, however, it was the king's turn to sacrifice his only daughter. There was no way to escape the dragon's evil clutches. Not even the king could do anything to stop this.

The entire royal family was extremely anxious and filled with sorrow. In a desperate attempt to find hope, the king announced to the village that whoever could save his daughter would inherit half of his kingdom, the title as crown prince, and his daughter.

Many people in his kingdom heard of his announcement but nobody was brave enough to take on the fearsome three-headed dragon.

One day, while the widow's son was out in the forest setting bird traps, he encountered a creature that was truly unbelievable. There were three people with three separate bodies who shared one single eye. The young man witnessed them tossing the eye to each other.

After playing around with the eye for a while, all three creatures grew tired and fell asleep. The young man crept up on them and stole their one eye while they were fast asleep. When they woke up, they could no longer see anything at all.

"Who stole our eye?" they shouted. The three creatures began to sniff around and picked up the young man's scent. "It has been a human who stole our eye!" they realized. "If you do not give it back to us, we cannot live! Please, if you give it back to us, we will give you anything you want."

The young man, who was still there, took this as his chance to carry out the king's bargain. "I want to inherit half of the king's land and marry his beautiful daughter. I can only do this by protecting his daughter from the terrifying *rul chuang ngei* who lives in a deep cave beyond our village."

One of the creatures reached into his bag and pulled out a bird trap. "You will take this and venture deep into the forest. Since it is far away from here, you will have to bring food and water for your journey. In the middle of the forest, you will find a magnificent and wide lake. In this lake, you will come across an even more magnificent colt from heaven. The colt flies down from the heavens and bathes in that lake. You will capture the colt with the bird trap that I have given you. When you capture the colt, it will grant you whatever wish you ask for. With this colt from heaven, you shall be able to carry out the king's bargain."

The young man gave the eye back to the creature and immediately returned home. He told his mother that he would go on a long trip. "The trip could possibly take four days. I have to bring food, water, and all the other necessities for my journey," he said.

So, after bidding his mother goodbye, the young man set off on his journey. He kept on going deeper and deeper into the forest, and just as the creature had told him, he came across a beautiful lake.

Suddenly, he spotted something that looked like a white bird in the lake. It was rather large for a bird. As the young man squinted closer to get a better look, he realized that it was not a bird at all, but the glorious colt from heaven!

After the colt had finished bathing, it trotted out of the water. All of a sudden, the colt was snagged in the bird trap set by the young man. It frantically flapped its bird-like wings, trying to escape, but in vain. The colt looked around and saw the young man.

"Why have you trapped me? How did you get this trap?" inquired the horse. The young man told the horse everything. "What do you want me to do?" the colt asked ungraciously. "The king's daughter is to be eaten by the *rul chuang ngei* very soon. I want to save her."

"I will help you. But first I must fly back to heaven," the colt told him. "I do not believe you. If you fly away, you will not return. I am sure of it," the young man countered. "No, no, I am not lying. It is only you humans that lie. I am a creature of dignity and honor," the colt neighed.

So, the great white colt flew back to the heavens, and, as he promised, returned immediately. He had brought with him a double-edged sword and a shield. "I will let you ride on me and you will tell me where the *rul chuang ngei* lives. With this sword, you will cut its heads. With this shield, you will protect yourself from its powerful fangs."

The young man got on the colt's back. "Do not be frightened no matter how high I fly. Even if you fall off, do not worry; I can pick you up again," the colt promised. As they reached the infamous cave of the dragon, the young man pointed towards it, gesturing that was their destination.

The colt flew down to the cave and the young man got off. He cautiously entered the cave but it was difficult to see where he was going, for the cave was nearly pitch black. A lingering smell of rotting flesh and noises of rattling bones filled the cave with even more mystery. The young man continued walking until he heard the undisturbed breathing of the dragon.

It was asleep. The young man slowly made his way closer towards the fierce beast. However, since the scent of humans was so distinct, the beast, even in his slumber, recognized it right away. It woke up with a start and let out a bellowing screech from each one of its fearsome mouths.

Before the dragon had time to attack, though, the young man brought his sword down and cut one of its heads. The creature writhed and screeched in pain. The young man quickly ran out of the cave and hopped on the colt's back. The colt flew the young man high up in the sky. Moments later, they flew back down and the young man attacked the dragon once more, cutting off its second head.

Again, the horse flew the young man high up in the sky. This time, before it flew back down, the colt warned the young man of something. "Now that you have cut off two of its heads, the *rul chuang ngei* will be ready to battle you. It is weaker now but you still must be careful."

When the colt flew back down, the *rul chuang ngei* was out of its cave and jumped onto the colt's back. The colt could not do anything anymore. The *rul chuang ngei* was now angrily spitting fire out of its one remaining mouth.

With the shield that the colt had given him, the young man protected himself from the dragon's fire. The colt flew very high up in the sky, this time up to the stars. Since it was flying immensely high, the dragon was beginning to shiver with fear.

The young man grabbed his double-edged sword with his two hands and cut off the third and final head of the dragon, thus causing the dragon to fall off and plummet to the ground. The ground that the dragon fell on turned into ashes. Those ashes withered away in the wind.

Now that the dragon was slain, it could no longer disturb the villagers! The colt flew the young man back to his village. "I have fulfilled your wish, human. What else is remaining for me to do?" asked the colt. "When I go to the king, how will he believe any word I say? It all sounds impossible," answered the young man.

"You will take out the bird trap from your bag and swing it. It will knock down all of the king's soldiers. The king will surely believe you then." Hence, the young man thanked the colt from heaven and watched it fly back to its home.

The young man went to the king, who was at the sacrificial stage. The young man saw that they had already tied the princess up in ropes. "You do not have to sacrifice your daughter, your highness. I have slayed the *rul chuang ngei*," said the young man.

The king was overjoyed to hear this but could not believe it. "How could a young man like you carry out such a dangerous and impossible task? What kind of a family are you from?" questioned the king.

The young man brought his mother and the king said to her, "I will have you both killed unless you give me proof that your son has slayed the *rul chuang ngei*." The old widow shook with fear, for she did not believe that her son could slay the beast. The young man was calm, however.

"Your highness, please make your soldiers stand in line," he said. The perplexed and amazed king made all his soldiers stand in line. Then, the young man took out the bird trap from his bag and swung it in the air.

Like the colt had said, it knocked down all the soldiers. The king and his subjects were all astonished to what they had just witnessed. "Your highness, I have done this to your soldiers and now only you remain. I have the power to kill you and inherit your kingdom, your throne, and your daughter. If you do not wish for this to happen, please keep your promise," said the young man.

The king was filled with joy. "I am very happy that a man like you will marry my daughter!" he cried. So, the king, as he promised, gave the young man half of his land, the title as crown prince, and his daughter, the princess.

The young man and the princess found happiness together and they all lived happily ever after.

The Bobcat and The Chickens

This tale is meant to be a nursery tale told to younger audiences. It has elements of humor and silliness. A family of chickens is stalked by a hungry bobcat. Unfortunately, the bobcat can never get his paws on the chickens. However, luck chooses to be on his side one day and he manages to eat every last one of the chickens. All except one egg. With the help of some friends, the little egg takes revenge on the bobcat for eating his family.

There once lived a family of chickens. They lived somewhat peacefully for a long time but soon, danger fell upon them. A bobcat who lived nearby had spotted the family of chickens and yearned to sink his teeth into their feathers. He tried every single day to catch and devour the chickens but to no luck.

He did not know where they lived, thus making it very difficult for him to catch them. What he didn't know was that the chickens had made their home in a large earthen jar. The mother of the family, the hen, told her children every night, "If the old bobcat asks you where we live, make sure to always lie about it. You will not tell the truth."

One evening, a little chick went to a nearby well to collect water. The bobcat saw her at the well and nimbly raced over to her. With a pleasant voice, the bobcat asked her, "Little chick, where are you and your family sleeping for the night?"

Forgetting her mother's words, the little chick answered truthfully. "We are sleeping in a big earthen jar, Mr. Bobcat. *Tak-ka-daak!*" The bobcat grinned slyly, revealing many sharp teeth. He turned around and ran back to his den.

'Tonight, I will feast on chicken!' he thought to himself with glee. The little chick, realizing she had let out their secret, ran frantically back to the earthen jar. "Mother! Mother! I encountered the old bobcat while I was collecting the water, but I accidentally told him where we lived!" she confessed. "Why didn't you obey my words, my dear? I told you every night! We are doomed now!" the hen clucked anxiously.

After thinking for a while, the hen finally concluded. "My children, Mr. Bobcat will come to our home at night and eat us all when he finds our earthen jar. So, we must not make any noise. If you need to let out gas, do not make it sound like '*poot!*' Make it sound like '*peet*' instead," she instructed her children.

Night's starry blanket covered the sky very soon and the family of chickens all nervously waited for the bobcat in their earthen jar. Sure enough, the bobcat arrived. He waited nearby, just in case one of them were to accidentally reveal their hiding spot but none did. So, the bobcat impatiently looked around.

A few minutes later, one of the chicks suddenly said, "Mother, I have to let out gas!" The hen nodded. "Remember, don't make it sound like '*poot!*' Make it sound like '*peet!*'" So, the little chick obediently let out a toot that sounded like '*peet!*'

Another few minutes passed and another one of the chicks suddenly said, "Mother, I have to let out gas!"

"Don't make it sound like '*poot!*'" Make it sound like '*peet!*'" So, the little chick obediently let out a toot that sounded like '*peet!*' Soon, a third chick said he needed to let out some gas. Again, the hen told him to make it sound like '*peet*' and not '*poot*.'

Much time passed and the bobcat was getting tired. He was getting ready to retreat and try again the next day. From inside the earthen jar, however, the hen told her chicks, "my children. I have to let out some gas, too."

Her chicks told her the same thing she told them: "Mother, remember not to make it sound like '*poot!*' Make it sound like '*peet!*'" The hen promised that she would. However, she must have been holding it for a long time, for when she let the gas out, it made such a loud '*poot*,' that the earthen jar shattered to pieces!

The bobcat let out a yowl of content and pounced on the chicks. In the blink of an eye, the bobcat gobbled up every last one of the chicks. The bobcat pounced on the hen, as well, but since she was bigger than her children, she had time to struggle some more.

The hen struggled to escape from the bobcat for quite some time. The poor hen was too exhausted to carry on and finally died. The bobcat ate her up, too. Now that he had devoured the entire family of chickens, the bobcat was very pleased and satisfied with himself. He joyfully marched back home.

Before the hen had died, though, she had left behind one egg. The egg had been late to hatch but the hen kept it just in case it would hatch later.

The egg, in the hen's struggle, had fallen out of its nest and it continuously rolled down a cliff. It kept on rolling downhill until it came across an army of *kohcik* (a dangerous type of ant; their bite is very painful).

"Little egg, where are you going?" asked the army of *kohcik*. "A bobcat ate my mother and my siblings. I am going to take revenge," answered the little egg. "We shall accompany you," said the army of *kohcik*. So, they followed.

After travelling for a bit, they came across a crab. "Little egg, *kohcik*, where are you going?" he asked. "We are going to take revenge on the old bobcat," they answered. "I shall accompany you," said the crab. So, he followed.

Soon, they came across a log trap. "Little egg, kohcik, crab, you are all going rather fast. Where are you going?" he asked. "We are going to take revenge on the old bobcat," they answered. "I shall accompany you," said the log trap. So, he followed.

They all kept on walking until they came across the bobcat's den. The sky turned a thick gray color and rain began to sprinkle on them. Soon, the gentle rain turned into a heavy shower and thunder rang across the sky.

"My friends, it is stormy now. We have to hurry. I will hide in his fireplace and wait for him. The little egg gave each of his friend a job. *Kohcik*, you all will sneak under his blanket and wait for him. Crab, you will go inside his bottle oil and wait for him. Log trap, you will stay nearby his house and wait for him outside."

Shortly after all of this, the bobcat returned to his house, wet from the rain. Much rain had fallen on him, so the bobcat was very cold. The bobcat blew on the fireplace to make the fire warmer, and the little egg threw some of the sparks in his eyes so that he was temporarily blinded.

'I will rub my eyes on the blanket so that I can see again,' the bobcat thought. When he tried to rub his eyes, however, the army of *kohcik* bit them so that they became all swollen and red. The bobcat yowled in pain and desperately tried to reach for his bottle of oil so that he could soothe the pain and rashes with the oil.

Little did he know that the crab was waiting for him. He reached inside the bottle of oil and let out yet another yowl of pain, for the crab had pinched his paws. "Aiyo! Aiyo!" he cried out. He ran out of the house and into the backyard, where the log trap was eagerly waiting for him.

The bobcat ran into the log trap and without knowing what force had done this to him, he instantly died. As soon as the bobcat perished, the little egg suddenly hatched! He was a small little chick. Since he no longer had his mother and siblings, he stayed with his friends who had helped him avenge his family.

The Tiger and the Dogs

*The Tiger and the Dogs, or Cakei le Uipi Farual, is the story
of two clever dogs and one cowardly tiger. With the mother
dog giving birth very soon and no shelter available except
for the den of a tiger, the dog couple plot a way to trick the
tiger. Their plan is not the most elaborate but to their luck,
the tiger is a cowardly fellow, and he falls for their trick.*

Once upon a time, there lived a family of dogs. One day,
as they were travelling, the mother dog's stomach began to
hurt. She was pregnant and her pups were to be delivered.
There was no safe shelter for them to rest, though.

As they carried on, the mother dog's stomach was in
profuse pain. Finally, they came across a tiger's den.
Cautiously, the dogs checked the den to see if the tiger was
there, and to their luck, he was not.

They rested in the den and eventually, the mother dog
gave birth to healthy pups. Soon after her pups were born, the
mother dog grew very anxious. "We are resting in a tiger's den.
He will come back sooner or later and when he does the tiger
will eat us all!" she said to her mate.

"Do not worry. If you do what I tell you to do, he will not eat us," replied the father dog. "What should we do? the mother dog asked.

"The minute the tiger is in sight, you will make our children cry. I will say loudly, 'Why did you let our children cry,' and you will reply so that the tiger can hear, 'They are crying because they want tiger meat.' Then, I will say, 'What a coincidence! A tiger is coming right now,' and you will say 'Hush, my children. Do not cry anymore, for your father will kill the tiger and he will bring back his meat.'"

Not long after that, the tiger did return to his den. Then, the mother dog made her children cry as they had planned. "Why did you let our children cry?" asked the father dog. "They are crying because they want tiger meat," she replied loudly. "What a coincidence! A tiger is coming right now!"

The cowardly tiger heard what they said and ran away in fear. He kept on running until he came across a clever monkey. The tiger told the monkey about his encounter with the family of dogs in his den.

"You are very lucky! You have meat that will last you a week!" exclaimed the monkey. The tiger shook his head frantically. "What do you mean 'lucky?' I heard them say that their pups were craving tiger meat! Their father shouted, 'A tiger is coming right now,' so I ran away before he could kill me and feed me to his children!"

To this, the monkey smacked the cowardly tiger on his head. "How stupid can you get? Who has ever beaten a fearsome tiger like you? Do you actually think a couple of dogs can kill you? Come on! I will go with you and you will kill all of them," the monkey said.

Reluctantly, the tiger led the monkey back to his den. The father dog spotted the two creatures making their way to the den. "Oh no! This time, we will be eaten by the tiger! The monkey has tempted the tiger to eat us!" he wailed to his mate.

"We will carry out our first plan and if that does not work, he will eat us all," said the mother dog. So, the mother dog made her children cry. "Why did you let our children cry?"

asked the father dog. "They are crying because they want tiger meat," she replied loudly. "How lucky you are, my children! A tiger and a monkey are coming right now! You will eat both tiger *and* monkey meat tonight!"

The cowardly tiger heard what they said and immediately dashed away in fear once more. The monkey chased after him and asked, "My friend, Tiger! Why did you flee?"

"What do you mean, 'Why did I flee?' You would flee, too, if you were to be eaten!" he replied. "A small dog cannot kill you! You are a tiger, much stronger than them!" The monkey kept on coaxing him.

"Alright, alright. Let us tie our tails together and go back," the tiger finally gave in. So, they went back. The father dog spotted the two creatures making their way to the den for a third time. "Oh no! This time, for sure, we will be eaten by the tiger!" He was rather frightened now.

The mother dog suggested they carry out the plan again. "If it does not work, we will surely be eaten up." As the tiger and the monkey came closer, the father dog shouted, "Why have you let our children cry again?"

"They are crying because they want tiger meat," the mother dog replied loudly. "Is that so? Well, the last time they came, the cunning monkey helped the tiger run away so I could not get them. This time, I will chase them until I catch them! I do not want my beloved children to cry any longer. Now, let me chase them!" he growled threateningly.

Filled with intense fear, the tiger turned around and ran as fast as his legs could carry him. The tiger's tail was still connected with the monkey's, so he dragged the monkey with him as he ran.

The monkey crashed into a big tree as they ran away. The tiger was nowhere to be seen again. So, the father dog chased after the monkey, killed him, and brought him back to the den to feed to his family. Hence, the family of dogs were safe.

Vompi and Phete

Vompi and Phete, like the Bobcat and the Chickens, is a nursery tale that is meant to be told to younger audiences. In this story, is a series of mischievous adventures and pranks all pulled by the cunning Phete. Vompi and Phete are good friends but because of Phete's mischievous personality, the two have an unsteady friendship. In the end, Vompi decides that he has put up with enough of Phete's tricks. The tables turn, and Vompi is the one who plays the last trick.

Long ago, there lived a big bear named Vompi and a little monkey named Phete. They were very good friends for a long time. Vompi was known to be a gullible and naïve fellow whereas Phete was known to be clever and mischievous. They were polar opposites but they got along.

One day, Phete said to his big friend, "Vompi, let us look for other friends to live together in one place." Thus, the two set off to find some new companions. They came across a hen, Arpi, and a beaver, Saihrem. All four of them became close friends and they lived together in one place.

They lived together for some time and all was well. One day, Phete suggested that each one of them start their own field and that they would all help one another with the fieldwork. So, they did just that.

"Let us go to Vompi's field and help him out," Phete said one day. "Vompi, you should make us a good lunch," Phete suggested. The four friends all worked hard in the field. When lunchtime drew near, Vompi told his friends, "I will prepare lunch for you all now," and went to his tent.

In the tent, Vompi lit the fire and pondered about what he would cook. He had no idea what to prepare for lunch, but eventually, he came up with an idea. He would roast his thighs and serve it to his friends.

First, he roasted his left thigh. After a bit, Vompi hit his thigh and exclaimed, "let a plateful of my fat come off," (in Chin, *"ka thau, kheng khat chuak"*) and it came off. Then, he roasted his right thigh. Again, Vompi hit his thigh and repeated what he said. Again, a plateful of his fat came off.

Vompi then prepared a delicious porridge out of his fat and happily served it to his friends. His friends consumed the porridge just as happily. "Wow, Vompi! This is a really good porridge!" his friends complimented him.

The next day, the four friends decided on going to Arpi's field. At her field, they all worked hard. When lunchtime drew near, Arpi told her friends, "I will prepare lunch for you all now," and went to her tent.

She laid some eggs, boiled them, and served them happily to her friends. "Wow, Arpi! Your lunch is just as good as Vompi's!" they complimented her.

The next day, they went to Saihrem's field. Like all the other times, they all worked hard in the field. When it was time for lunch, Saihrem caught them fish from the river and served them happily to his friends. "Wow, Saihrem! This fish is so fresh!" they all complimented him once more.

It was time to go to Phete's field the next day. They worked hard in the field, as usual, but when it was time for lunch, Phete did not know what to serve his friends. "Vompi made his porridge out of his fat, so why can't I?" he said to himself.

Then, he roasted his thighs and hit them, exclaiming, "let a plateful of my fat come off," but instead of his fat coming off, his thighs were burnt by the fire. So, Phete decided he would got to the river and catch fish like Saihrem. He dove into the river and flailed around, trying to catch some fish. In the end, however, he caught nothing.

Finally, Phete made up his mind to lay eggs like Arpi. So, Phete squated down and gave a forceful push. Instead of eggs coming out, however, his dung came out. His other friends would never have even considered the thought of serving dung to each other, but Phete, being the mischievous little critter that he was, decided that was just what he would do.

Phete made some porridge, mixed his dung in it, and served it to his friends. Before even eating it, his friends noticed the distinct smell of something putrid. "Phete, your lunch smells rather odd," they pointed out. Phete shook his head. "Ah, it's just *buhrumthu* (a type of fermented soy that has a somewhat bad smell)."

So, his friends ate the porridge but he did not. As they finished up eating the porridge, Phete let out a gleeful laugh and shouted, "I lied! It's not *buhrumthu*, it was my dung! Dung-eaters! Dung-eaters!" With that, he dashed away from his friends.

His friends were all very angry that they had been humiliated like that, so they chased after him. "Phete is not a good friend. We will no longer be friends with him anymore. I will catch him and kill him. We will eat his meat," Vompi said to his friends.

"Phete is too clever and mischievous. There is no way you will ever catch him," said Arpi and Saihrem. "No, I will catch him no matter what," he retorted.

One day, Vompi called, "Phete!" From inside his house, Phete answered "Yes?"

"Will you go the field tomorrow, Phete?"

"Yes, I will!"

"Which path will you take? The mountain path or the river path?"

"River path!"

Vompi grinned to himself and waited eagerly in the river path. Little did he know that Phete had tricked him! He had taken the mountain path. Rather disappointed, Vompi returned home, planning to catch him the next day.

"Phete!" called Vompi the next day. "Yes?" replied Phete from inside his house.

"Will you go to the field tomorrow, Phete?"

"Yes, I will!"

"Which path will you take? The mountain path or the river path?"

"Mountain path!"

So, Vompi eagerly waited for Phete in the mountain path. Again, Phete had tricked him. He had taken the river path. The disappointed Vompi returned home but he now knew Phete's trick. For the third time, Vompi called, "Phete!" Phete answered from inside his home, "yes?"

"Will you go to the field tomorrow, Phete?"

"Yes, I will!"

"Which path will you take? The mountain path or the river path?"

"River path!"

This time, Vompi waited for him in the mountain path. To Vompi's content, Phete had, in fact, taken the mountain path. He managed to catch Phete. "I will kill you now!" Vompi bellowed. "Wait, wait! My good friend, Vompi, I was simply trying to cook you a chicken!" he protested cunningly.

"Oh! Really? Well, in that case, I will spare your life," Vompi said gladly. Phete and Vompi went back to Phete's house, where Phete did actually serve Vompi chicken. "Now, we will be friends again. We will not fight or quarrel, anymore, okay?" Phete said pleasantly. "Okay!" agreed Vompi foolishly.

One day, Phete went to a nearby hill and discovered a beehive. The beehive was home to an army of extremely violent bees. Phete covered the openings of the beehive so that none of the bees could get out.

When he knocked on the beehive, Phete could hear the angry buzzing of the bees. He brought the beehive home and placed it near his house. Vompi was visiting Phete the next day, when Phete said, "Vompi, I have this interesting new instrument. It makes a buzzing sound whenever you hit it. Why don't you try? Hit it gently."

He gave the beehive to Vompi, who softly knocked on it. He heard a faint, but distinct buzzing sound. "Wow, this instrument has a nice sound," Vompi said. "Climb up to the top of the hill and when I say 'Hit it,' you will hit the instrument as hard as you can. That way, it will make a beautiful sound that can be heard from miles away!" Phete suggested.

Vompi climbed the hill without knowing Phete's true intention. When he reached the top of the hill, Phete shouted, "Hit it!" The naïve Vompi hit the beehive as hard as he could, ripping the cover off. The furious bees that had been trapped inside of their hive for so long, came flying out and stung Vompi everywhere they could.

Vompi tried to run away but the bees followed, stinging him without mercy. Phete fell to the ground and laughed at his friend as he was chased by the violent army of bees. 'This Phete really is a bad friend! I will catch him and eat him up for sure!' Vompi thought angrily.

Like before, Vompi tried to catch the mischievous Phete by asking him which path he would take. Phete managed to trick him twice once more but on the third time, Vompi caught him. "Wait, wait! My good friend, Vompi, I was simply trying to cook you a beaver!" he protested cunningly.

"Oh! Really? Well, in that case, I will spare you!" Vompi relented. Phete led him back to his house and served him beaver. They were friends once again and Vompi was no longer angry.

One day, Phete went to the forest and carved a *tikuang* (a big, wooden water container). As he was carving it, Vompi strolled up to him. "Phete, what are you doing?" he asked. "Oh, I was carving this *kuang* (container) for you!" Phete replied. "You can sleep here at night and it will be warm and comfortable for you! Come here, let me see if you fit in here," Phete said.

Without thinking, Vompi climbed into the container and lay down. Quickly, Phete covered the lid and tied it up. Ignoring Vompi's banging of the roof of the container, Phete pushed him over a cliff.

Miraculously, Vompi survived the fall. However, he was beyond angry now. "No more excuses! Phete is a terrible friend! I will definitely kill him!" he roared.

For a third time, Vompi tried to catch Phete by asking him which path he would take. However, Phete, too, had come up with a new trick. If he said "mountain path," he would actually take the mountain path. If he said "river path," he would actually take the river path. Thus, Vompi could not catch him.

One day, Phete was collecting thatch in the forest. Vompi spotted him and angrily raced towards him, ready to kill his former friend in one blow. But Phete shook his head frantically. Wait, wait! My good friend, Vompi! You do not understand! I was simply trying to collect this thatch for you!" he pleaded.

"I will bundle this thatch for you and you will carry it on your back. I will tell you where to go by saying 'north' or 'south,' and it will grow bigger and bigger. That way, you will have plenty to cover your roof."

Vompi had not been expecting this, so he agreed to it. As he carried the thatch on his back, Phete secretly lit it on fire!

"Vompi, to the south, to the south! Vompi, to the north, to north!" he yelled.

Just as few moments passed and Vompi suddenly began to feel the heat of the fire on his fur. He turned back to see that a huge fire was engulfing the thatch on his back. Vompi ran around and roared in pain, for the flames were spreading to his back.

Eventually, he found a swamp and jumped in, rolling around until the flames were extinguished. By then, he was very dizzy and no longer thinking straight. Phete ran up to him, and, wanting to know whether Vompi still had a right mind, said, "if you are conscious, bite my finger." He held out his finger but Vompi made no attempt to bite it.

"If you are conscious, bite my toes," and he held out his toes but Vompi did not respond. "If you are conscious, bite my head," and he held out his head. In the blink of an eye, Vompi opened his jaws and bit down on Phete's head, killing him.

An Old Tiger (Cakei Tar)

An Old Tiger is the story about a quick-witted monkey and a big old tiger. Due to his undying curiosity, the monkey finds himself in the hungry grasp of the old tiger. However, thinking fast, he manages to escape death. Twice this happens but by the third time, they are on friendly terms with each other. Or so thought the old tiger. The monkey puts together an elaborate plan to get rid of the tiger once and for all.

Long ago, there was once an old tiger who lived isolated in a big, dark cave. In his youth, the tiger was an excellent hunter. However, he was so old now, that he could not hunt for himself anymore. The tiger never left his cave and fed on the thoughtless little critters that stumbled into his cave every now and then. He was always very hungry.

One day, a curious monkey peeked into the old tiger's cave. Before the monkey had a chance to run away, the old tiger caught him. "I am old and unable to hunt anymore. I am very grateful that you came in. You will make a fine dinner tonight," the old tiger said in a scratchy voice.

Now, the monkey was not only curious, he was a clever thing, too. "Oh, Master Tiger! When you were young, you feasted on delicious animals and you were never hungry. How could you even consider eating me? My meat will not taste good at all!" he protested. "Can you see that deer over there? Don't you want to eat it instead?" the monkey pointed at a deer just a few lengths away from the cave.

"Of course, I would rather eat it!" the tiger replied as if he was foolish to even ask. "But I am too old and I will not be able to catch it," he added miserably. "Do not worry! I can bring the deer to you," the monkey exclaimed. "If you can do that, you will be spared," the old tiger agreed.

So, the monkey went over to the deer. "Hello, my friend! I have something I need to tell you. Please wait for me," he greeted pleasantly. The deer, who was about to walk away, waited for the monkey. "Yes, what is it?'

"Do you see that cave over there?" asked the monkey.

"Yes, I can see it. Why?"

"In there, an old tiger who was on the brink of death, told me he would tell me his will before he died. I think you deserve to be the one who should hear the old tiger's will."

The deer was rather bewildered. "What kind of a will is it?" he questioned. "I think it might be about his strength and victory," the monkey responded. The deer smiled to himself when he heard this.

"Well, hurry up! Get in the cave, quickly! The old tiger might die before you do!" the monkey jumped up and down. So, the unfortunate deer eagerly dashed into the cave. The minute the deer entered the cave, the tiger sank his teeth into its neck and devoured it.

After some time had passed, the monkey, curious to know whether the tiger was dead or not, peeked into the cave once more. Again, the tiger caught him. "The deer you brought me was enjoyable but I am hungry again. I will eat you now!" the tiger said.

"Wait, Master Tiger! Don't you want to eat that elk over there? It will be much more tasteful than I!" the monkey pointed to a nearby elk. "Of course, I would rather eat it!"

"Do not worry! I can bring the elk to you!"

"Do that and I will spare you."

So, the monkey went to the elk. "Hello, my friend! I have something I need to tell you. Please wait for me," he called. "Yes, what is it?" said the elk.

"Do you see that cave over there?" said the monkey, pointing to the cave.

"Yes, I can see it. Why?"

"In there, an old tiger who was on the brink of death, told me that he wants to pass on his strength and victory to me. I said to the tiger, 'But doesn't that elk over there seem much more fitting than I do,' and he said, 'That elk would not want to come over here. I will just pass it on to you.' So, I said 'I will go and check with him first. If he is not interested, you can pass it on to me.' That is why I came over here."

The elk ran as fast as his slender legs could carry him into the cave, eager to inherit such greatness. As soon as he ran into the cave, the tiger latched his teeth onto the elk's neck, ready to snap it in half.

To his dismay, the elk managed to break free and ran away, even faster than before. Furious that the monkey had tricked him, the elk told him that he would kill him. "Wait, my friend! What did Master Tiger do to you in the cave?" the monkey pretended to be confused.

"He tried to eat me! He bit down onto my neck and almost killed me!" the elk exclaimed in a great rage. "Oh, you don't understand, my friend! He was simply trying to whisper it into your ear!" the monkey explained.

The elk thought about it for a while and concluded that what the monkey said made sense. 'When he wrapped his paws around my neck and positioned his jaws next to my ears he was just trying to tell me his secret in a whisper,' the elk pondered.

So, he decided to go back into the cave, with the belief that it was all just a simple misunderstanding. As the elk entered the cave, the old tiger instantly latched onto his neck and sank his sharp teeth into the elk's flesh.

After this, the old tiger and the monkey became close friends. The tiger did not have any reason to suspect that his friend the monkey would be trying to betray him. However, that was exactly what the monkey was plotting.

One day, the monkey tried to tempt the tiger. "My good friend, Tiger, I spotted a tiger that looks exactly like you who claimed that he was the strongest tiger ever and that nobody could ever defeat him. But I told him, 'I have a good tiger friend who is very strong. I bet he can beat you easily.' Then, that tiger challenged you by saying, 'If he dares, tell him to come and fight me!'"

Upon hearing this, the old tiger was filled with a great rage. "Who is stronger than I? Where is this rival? Take me to him so I can rip him to shreds!" he roared angrily. Then, the monkey led the old tiger out of his cave and up a very high cliff.

They came to a stop when the monkey told the tiger to look down. As the old tiger looked down, he saw another tiger that looked almost identical to him. It was his reflection! "Is this the tiger that challenged me?" he growled, not knowing it was his own reflection.

"Yes, it is, my friend! Look at how defiant he looks! He does not fear you at all. Raise your paw, he will do the same!" said the monkey. As the tiger raised his paw, he saw the other tiger do the same. This farther angered the tiger, who thought it was mocking him.

"See, my friend? He copies whatever you do! That means he has no respect for you at all. He's mocking you," the monkey pressed. "How dare he?" bellowed the furious old tiger. Without thinking, he leapt from the cliff and plummeted towards the river below.

The monkey watched as the old tiger's limp body was swept down with the current, grinning with satisfaction the entire time.

Than Cer's Story

Sharing similar elements with the tale of Cinderella, Man Vang's Story tells the tale of Than Cer, a kindhearted young girl with a devoted, wealthy father. After her mother passes away from illness and her father is chosen to fight in the war, Than Cer is left in the hands of her cruel stepmother and stepsister. Life is already dreadful for Than Cer but her stepmother, who wished her dead, plots a scheme to end her life once and for all. To her father's great rage and sorrow, the stepmother's plan was a success. This tale ends on a sad note.

During the time when there were many bloody civil wars in Chin State, there lived a kind, wealthy man and his lovely wife and daughter. They were a blissful family and nothing could ever come between them. Nothing but death alone. But the man's lovely wife soon grew ill and passed away, leaving only him and their beautiful young daughter, Than Cer. The wealthy man treasured his daughter very much and feared that she would become lonely without the love of a mother.

So, he decided to marry again. Unfortunately, the woman he married was very vile, callous, cold-hearted. She had a daughter who was the same age as Than Cer. She, too, was just as evil as her mother.

A few months after their marriage, the man was chosen to fight in battle. Although he did not want to leave his beloved daughter behind during such a time, it was mandatory for him to go.

Cruel, bloody wars were taking place and it was very dangerous for children to be without a parent or guardian. But he figured his new wife would take good care of Than Cer. After all, she was always so benevolent and caring to her.

After promising to be back as soon as he could, the man kissed his daughters and wife and set off. As soon as he was gone, Than Cer's stepmother violently struck her head with the back of her hand without any reason. The poor girl looked up at her stepmother and sister with the most pitiful expression, interlaced with fear and disbelief.

"You are no daughter of mine. Behave yourself and keep quiet or else you shall suffer severe consequences," Than Cer's stepmother threatened heartlessly.

For many days, Than Cer's stepmother and stepsister tormented her and made her do all the chores. When she rested just slightly, they pulled on her pretty black hair and forced her back to work. When she cried, they beat her endlessly.

Than Cer was exhausted and worn-out. She could scarcely open her eyes. But her stepmother and her stepsister gave her no rest. "Lazy, idiot girl! Get back to work!" they screamed. They were malicious and had absolutely no pity on Than Cer. They despised her and wished her dead so that they could inherit all the wealth.

One day, Than Cer's stepmother ordered her to go and collect firewood from the battlefield. "But why the battlefield, stepmother? There is a war going on. What if there is a battle when I am collecting the firewood?" Than Cer asked.

Her stepmother struck her face aggressively. "Don't question what I tell you to do! If I say do it, you do it. Now go!" she demanded. Than Cer sorrowfully trudged outside as her stepsister sneered at her in the rudest way. Poor Than Cer began to sob her heart out as soon as she was out of earshot. She wept and wept so loud and miserably that a few of the neighbors looked outside to gaze forlornly at her.

Than Cer had a best friend. She was a sweet, empathetic girl and when she heard Than Cer's cry, she went to console her. "Dear Than Cer, what's wrong? Why are you so sad? Please wipe those tears away, I can't bear to see you in such a dreadful state," she said softly.

When Than Cer told her what she had been through and what her stepmother wanted her to do, she embraced her tightly. "Oh, Than Cer. Don't go to the battlefield. You will surely die. They are having a battle there today and tomorrow! Didn't your stepmother know about it?"

"She probably did. My stepmother doesn't care about me. She wants me to die. I am sure that she sent me to the battlefield so I could be killed," Than Cer said. Her friend hugged her once more and wiped her tears away. "Listen, I have plenty of firewood in my house. Don't go to the battlefield and risk your life. I shall give you my firewood to take home," she said.

Gratefully, Than Cer accepted and returned home with a bundle of firewood. The minute Than Cer entered the house, her stepmother smacked her across the face and broke her firewood, beating her savagely with it. "I told you to go to the *battlefield* and collect firewood, not to your friend's house! I know this isn't firewood from the battlefield! You cannot fool me!" she screamed.

That night, Than Cer was sent to her room without any dinner.

The next morning, Than Cer's stepmother called her again and told her to go to the battlefield to collect water from the river. "Stepmother, there is a battle going on there, isn't there? Please don't make me go. I will collect water from anywhere else but please not from the battlefield!"

Again, her stepmother forced her to go and collect the water anyway. Than Cer sobbed the entire way. Her loving friend came out again and offered to give her water but this time, Than Cer refused. "No, I'm sorry. Last night, my stepmother nearly murdered me for bringing home the firewood you gave me. If I do it again, she will surely kill me. Pray that I survive."

Her friend begged her not to go, but Than Cer went to the battlefield to collect the water. The field was bloodstained and a murder of crows were feeding hungrily on the rotting corpses that littered the grounds, but it was empty otherwise. Cautiously, Than Cer made her way to the fresh river and began to collect the water.

Without any warning, something grabbed her from behind. She was too frightened to scream, but she struggled to escape. "What are you doing here?" a voice whispered. Than Cer turned around and faced a young boy about her age dressed in a soldier's uniform.

"My stepmother ordered me to collect water from the battlefield. She would have killed me if I didn't," Than Cer explained. The soldier boy looked at her in disbelief. "Well, you will be killed *here* if you stay! Quick, collect the water and run back to your house without ever stopping to look back!" he insisted.

Than Cer did as she was told and nimbly exited the battlefield in one piece. She told her friend the good news on the way back and the two did a quick celebration by hugging and crying joyfully. But the happiness did not last long. When Than Cer returned home, she was welcomed by yet another beating.

"How impudent and disgraceful can you get?" her stepmother said furiously. "No, no, I *did* go to the battlefield and I *did* collect water from the river there," Than Cer sobbed.

Her stepmother poured the water she had collected over her and accused her of lying.

"You are a disobedient child! Go back right now and collect the water from the battlefield!" the stepmother shouted. In a flood of tears, Than Cer dashed out of the house. Her friend tried to help her again but Than Cer refused. "I'm sorry. I have no choice. This time, I don't want anybody's help. My stepmother will torture me! So, don't even bother praying that I make it out alive!" Than Cer wept.

The friends embraced each other for the very last time, and, Than Cer took off. When she arrived at the battlefield, it was dead silent and empty. Not a single person was in sight. Vigilantly, Than Cer made her way to the river and collected the water. It was much harder now that it was dark out.

All of a sudden, a loud gunshot rang throughout the battlefield and the soldiers all erupted from their hiding spots, firing at each other. Than Cer shut her eyes and plugged her ears, curling up into a ball as tightly as she could. She heard an ear-piercing gunshot and then, all was silent. She took one final breath and tumbled to the ground in a pool of her own crimson blood.

Her father returned home the very next day, eager and upbeat to see his beloved daughter again. He raced to his house as fast as his legs could carry him, and burst through the door, expecting to be welcomed by his young daughter's affectionate hug and kiss.

However, there was nothing of the sort. Instead, his wife and stepdaughter welcomed him with insincere words and smiles. "Where is my daughter?" he asked. Than Cer's stepsister stepped up teasingly. "Here I am, father!" The man shook his head, troubled. "Where is my sweet Than Cer?"

Than Cer's stepmother and stepsister glanced at each other awkwardly. "Ah, Than Cer is at her friend's house spending the night," the stepmother lied. The man stood up and began to walk out of the house. "Where are you going, my love?" asked his wife.

"I miss my daughter very much. I am going to her friend's house to pick her up." At this, the stepmother and her daughter started protesting and trying to convince him to stay. But the man had made up his mind. He walked over to Than Cer's friend's house and knocked on the door. Than Cer's kind friend opened the door but her face was wet with tears.

"Do you know where my daughter is?" the man inquired gently. Than Cer's friend broke down into uncontrollable sobbing when she heard Than Cer's name. "I do not know. She didn't come to me last night like she used to," she admitted. So, the man went back to his house and asked again where Than Cer was.

"Er, she just came back and went looking for you at her friend's house," the stepmother lied. Again, the man went back to Than Cer's friend's house and questioned where she was. "She didn't come. I have told you, Sir. I do not know where she is."

The man was deeply troubled now. He went back to the house and demanded to know what had really happened. The stepmother and her daughter tried all sorts of lies but the man demanded to know the truth. They were very scared now, as he was getting angry and impatient. Finally, the stepsister gave in.

"She's dead, she's dead! Her body is still in the battlefield and her blood is still spilling in the river! My mother killed her by ordering her to go and collect the water. This was not by accident, but on purpose!" the stepsister confessed.

Her mother stared at her in a medley of spite and fear. Then, she tried to run out of the house. But her husband caught up with her and in a rage of fury, he killed her with a dagger. The stepsister shrieked when she saw this and ran far, far away.

The man immediately rushed to the battlefield and looked for his daughter. As the stepsister had said, Than Cer's body was still there and her blood was still spilling in the river. He wept endlessly and carried her graceful body back to the house.

Without burying Than Cer's body, the man took the dagger he had killed his wife with, and ended his own life.

Ngun Nu and Her Sister

Ngun Nu and Her Sister tells the tale of two beautiful sisters who were separated due to an unfortunate incident. Ngun Nu is reincarnated into an elegant white crane, while her sister mourns her as dead. Feeling sorry for her sister, Ngun Nu invites her to join her flock as a crane. However, even after being given specific instructions on how to survive, Ngun Nu's sister accidentally plummets to her death.

In many ages past, there lived a poor family in the depths of Chin hills. The family had two lovely daughters. Ngun Nu, their eldest daughter, was soft-spoken and compassionate. She had a reputation for being a generous beauty. Her younger sister was just as beautiful, but she was feisty, ill-tempered, and selfish. She always desired everything, despite the fact that they were tremendously poor. It was on one specific occasion that her selfishness led to an unnecessary tragedy.

One blustery morning, just a little while before the friendly sun had woken from its slumber, the parents of the two sisters told them to go to the field to do some work. Ngun Nu and her sister did as they were told and worked until midday when the sun had come out from behind the thick gray clouds.

The sun shone rather brightly on the sisters, tiring them and making them perspire. "Sister, it's much too hot to be working right now. Let's take a break to look for some white cucumbers," Ngun Nu suggested. "Gladly!" The girls dropped their tools and raced around, looking for some juicy, tasteful white cucumbers to consume. White cucumbers were the tastiest of the cucumbers and it was very rare to find one.

Luckily, Ngun Nu's younger sister managed to snag a sizeable one from the ground in just a few minutes. How mouth-watering it looked! The young girl began to nibble on her cucumber, savoring the delicious flavor. Ngun Nu, unfortunately, only found a diminutive green cucumber, that had absolutely no flavor to it. She tried to look around for more, but realized that her search was pointless and futile. She frowned at her own and glanced over to see her sister's amazing white cucumber.

"Sister, please let me take a bite," she pleaded. Ngun Nu's sister scowled at her and turned her head away greedily. "Find your own! There's plenty around here," was the reply. "But there isn't. There's only one good cucumber in this field and it's the one you're holding. Please, I'm hungry, too. We've been working since daybreak."

"No!"

"Please, our parents told us to share ever since we were little kids."

"Which is exactly why I won't share with you. Besides, our parents aren't here right now; they won't know."

Ngun Nu saw that she had no chance of getting anywhere with this rational pleading tactic. She waited a little longer and her stomach grumbled and growled like never before. Her sister had been nibbling little bits of the cucumber and by now, it was almost gone. Ngun Nu realized that if she didn't do something soon, she wouldn't get a chance to eat food for the rest of the day.

So, she stood up and walked over to a fresh, muddy patch of soil. The soil was actually a new termite nest, sticky, and almost inescapable if you were covered. This was known as, 'Chuncunghlum.'

Chuncunghlum, according to Chin folklore, was considered to be tied with the devil and demons. If you chanted, "Oh, Chuncunghlum, swallow me, swallow me," (in Chin, *Chuncunghlum aw ka seng, ka seng*) he would slowly, but effectively swallow you until you had nowhere to move, breathe, or live.

"Sister, if you don't share the white cucumber with me, I'll chant to Chuncunghlum and he will swallow me," Ngun Nu warned. To this, the younger sister laughed scornfully. "Go ahead and do that! Then I won't have to worry about any sister bossing me around and telling me how I should live!" she didn't even bother to turn herself around to look at her sister.

Now, really, the younger sister just assumed it was some sort of a trick to get her to share. Ngun Nu couldn't believe her ears. Was her sister really this ignorant and greedy? Wistfully, Ngun Nu chanted, "Oh, Chuncunghlum, swallow me, swallow me, for my sister won't share her white cucumber with me" (in Chin, *Chuncunghlum aw ka seng, ka seng; ka nau nih zil sai rang a ka cheu duh lo e*).

When she finished this chant, Chuncunghlum swallowed her up to her ankle. Again, she asked, "Sister, please share the remaining bits of the white cucumber with me." Again, the younger sister replied selfishly, "No way! Find your own!" So Ngun Nu chanted again, "*Chuncunghlum aw ka seng, ka seng; ka nau nih zil sai rang a ka cheu duh lo e.*" Chuncunghlum swallowed her up to her knees.

"Sister, please share the remaining bits of the cucumber with me," Ngun Nu pleaded. "Nope." Once more, Ngun nu chanted, "*Chuncunghlum aw ka seng, ka seng; ka nau nih zil sai rang a ka cheu duh lo e.*" Chuncunghlum swallowed her up to her stomach. "Now will you share with me, sister?" she asked again. Still believing it was some sort of a trick, the younger sister shook her head in rejection.

"Chuncunghlum aw ka seng, ka seng; ka nau nih zil sai rang a ka cheu duh lo e." Now Chuncunghlum had swallowed Ngun Nu up to her neck. She squirmed around and struggled for breath. "Please share the remaining bits of the white cucumber with me."

By this time, Ngun Nu's sister finally began to show some concern. Pacing herself, she turned to face her older sister neck-deep and trapped in the Chuncunghlum. The younger sister almost gave in but she immediately avoided eye contact and once again refused to share it.

"I know it's all just a trick, stop fooling around and get out of there before something happens," she said firmly. Ngun Nu shook her head to the best of her ability. "It's not a trick. I promise." Ngun Nu assured her sister calmly. "Yes, it is!" Ngun Nu's sister squawked. A brief, but painful silence passed by, followed by *"Chuncunghlum aw ka seng, ka seng; ka nau nih zil sai rang a ka cheu..."*

The younger sister cut her off. "Okay! I am sorry! I'll share the cucumber with you!" she turned around again, her arms ready to pry her sister out of the termite nest and embrace her. However, when she turned around, neither Ngun Nu nor Chuncunghlum were anywhere to be found. A couple strands of beautiful silky hair as black as the darkest twilight took her place. Another silence passed, this one even more painful than the silence before.

As if to answer some secret signal, the younger sister shrieked in agonizing remorse. The young girl clawed furiously at the ground, desperately trying to help her sister get out. She knew it was no use, though. She sobbed in uncontrollable sorrow, praying so hard for forgiveness. It was a pitiful sight.

Weeping the entire way home, Ngun Nu's younger sister vowed that if there was a way to somehow retrieve her beloved sister from the dead, she would. Even if it meant giving up her own life.

After the death of her sister, Ngun Nu's younger sister spent most of her time weeping in sorrow and remorse. One day, she sat under a tree, sobbing her heart away like she always did. She wiped her tears away as she heard a medley of goose-like honking above her. The younger sister glanced upwards to see a flock of beautiful white cranes flying in the open sky.

They looked ever so majestic and wise. Without thinking, Ngun Nu's younger sister called to them, "Oh, all the cranes that fly over me, have you seen my sister, Ngun Nu?" To her surprise they answered her! "Yes, we've seen your sister. She is still alive. But she is in the far South, cleaning up after cow and ox dung."

Ngun Nu's younger sister found this hard to believe and waited until another flock of cranes passed by. Again, she asked, "Oh, all the cranes that fly over me, have you seen my sister, Ngun Nu?" Now, the younger sister did not know it, but Ngun Nu had been reincarnated into the body of a white crane. She so happened to be a part of the flock of cranes flying above her.

When she heard her sister's voice, Ngun Nu thought to herself, "That sounds very much like my sister!" She looked down and gasped as she realized the voice, did, in fact, belong to her sister. Ngun Nu flew down, and she embraced her sister tightly and revealed that it was her. The younger sister apologized over and over again, and Ngun Nu warmly smiled, accepting her apologies.

"If only I could follow you! It's so miserable and lonely here without you," the younger sister sighed. Ngun Nu quickly flew back up to her flock and asked them, "Please, each of you take off one feather so my sister can become one of us." The cranes all jubilantly flew down and attached their feathers on Ngun Nu's younger sister, giving her majestic wings of her own.

They guided her across the sky and helped her whenever she grew unsteady. "Where are we going?" she questioned Ngun Nu. "We are on our way to our home. There you can turn into a real crane, like the rest of us," she explained. "Listen carefully. Whenever you come across a small river, make sure to exclaim loudly, 'Oh! It is quite a big river!' And whenever you come across a big river, make sure to always exclaim loudly 'Oh! It is quite a small river!'" Ngun Nu instructed her carefully.

Her younger sister promised to do just that before Ngun Nu flew faster to catch up with the rest of the cranes. Ngun Nu's sister did as she was instructed to do for a while and everything was going well. They had almost arrived to their new home when they came across another river. This one was a large river, but the younger sister accidentally exclaimed, "Oh! It is quite a big river!"

With this, her glorious wings began to wither away and the beautiful white feathers rapidly fell off, creating an exquisite but dangerous whirlwind. The younger sister screamed and begged for help as she began falling down towards the big river, but nobody could help her. They were all too far away to catch her before she fell.

So, Ngun Nu's sister plunged into the depths of the river beneath her and a huge fish, mistaking her as a fallen crane, devoured her.

Man Vang and Man Bo

The story of Mang Vang and Man Bo is usually seen as a Cinderella story, but there are some elements to the tale that are rather different from Cinderella. Man Vang is a beautiful young girl with a kind heart, whose life was somewhat normal until her mother passes away from a sudden illness. Her father remarries a cruel witch with a cruel daughter. After meeting the man of her dreams, it seems as though Man Vang's pitiful life will be turned around. But her stepmother and stepsister refuse to let her have peace. Man Vang has to go through a series of unpleasant adventures to reunite with the love of her life. This tale involves quite a bit of violence and gore, so it is recommended for older audiences.

Many years ago, there lived a poor couple who had a beautiful young daughter. They named her Man Vang. Man Vang was an exquisite young girl, from the time she was a small infant to when she became a mature young woman. She had a gorgeous, pale face and her pretty chocolate-colored eyes twinkled charmingly almost all the time. Her body structure was near perfect. Moreover, Man Vang was a very obedient and kindhearted girl, so everybody in the village admired her.

Man Vang's parents loved her dearly and were both very proud of her. The family had to work in the fields most of the time in order to grow and sell their crops. One day, Man Vang's mother suddenly grew very ill.

She was ill to the point where she could not even get out of her bed. Time passed and the illness was too much for her mother to bear and she died. They buried her body in the backyard, and from her grave, a beautiful flower grew.

The flower bloomed and whenever people saw its petals they always thought, 'What a beautiful little flower.' Humans were not the only ones who thought the flower was pretty. One day, a little Lasi (fairies in Chin mythology) plucked the flower, and brought it with her to a lake. The Lasi cast a spell on the flower so that it transformed into a *lim* (python). The python possessed the ability to take the form of Man Vang's mother again.

Her mother's death upset both Man Vang and her father very much but Man Vang made sure it did not keep her from being the kindhearted girl she was. Now that her mother had passed away, the father and daughter only had each other. Man Vang took care of her father and the two regularly went to the field to work.

One day, as Man Vang and her father were returning home from a day's work in the field, Man Vang's father ordered her to collect fire from their neighbor's house. Now, their neighbor was a spiteful woman who was secretly a witch.

She had nothing better to do than criticize and ridicule people. She had a daughter named Man Bo who was just as spiteful and cruel as her mother. She was remarkably ugly, too.

Her face was hideous by itself, but to add to it, she was scarred with pock-marks. The widow had had her eyes on Man Vang's father for a long time.

Man Vang went to the witch's house as she was told. "Hello, Aunty. Hello, Man Bo. I have come to ask if you could lend us some of your fire," Man Vang asked gently. The witch saw this as her small chance to marry Man Vang's father. "I suppose I could lend you some," she paused, "if and only if your father agrees to marry me."

Confused and slightly amused, Man Vang ran back to her father and told him about what the witch had proposed. Her father, to her surprise, agreed to marrying the witch. What she didn't know was that the witch had secretly cast a love spell on her father. So, Man Vang rushed back to the witch's house and told her how her father had replied.

Of course, the witch gave Man Vang the fire and promised to be at their house by dinner. Delighted, the witch began to pack up her things. At dinner, the witch and her daughter barged into Man Vang's house. Although Man Vang was very upset about it, her father showed no sign of discomfort because he was under the spell cast by the witch.

Man Vang's father was married to the witch. As he was under the spell, Man Vang's father was indifferent and uncaring towards her. Moreover, Man Vang was despised by her stepmother and stepsister for being so kindhearted and beautiful. They were immensely jealous of her and even wished her dead. So, they treated her horribly, beating her, scolding her, and forbidding her to have any friends.

Her stepmother took it so far that she prohibited her from eating the good food. They gave her small grains of rice and, if she was lucky, a few leftover pieces of meat that clung onto the bones. She treated Man Bo and Man Vang so differently. To Man Vang, she berated and beat her, but to Man Bo, she provided delicious food and spent all her money buying beautiful garments and jewelry for her to wear.

Man Vang's father was still under the spell and he paid no attention to the fact that his new wife and daughter were treating his own daughter in this way.

Man Vang was so distressed and saddened about her new life, that one day, she went down to the lake where her mother had turned into a *lim*, sat down, and wept. "Mother, Mother, I miss you so much!" she sobbed pitifully. Now, her mother, the python, heard her miserable cries and quickly appeared to her.

She explained that she was Man Vang's mother and how she came to be this way. She sat beside her and comforted her, providing her with pleasant foods to eat. Because of this, Man Vang was much more relieved and every single day, she went to the river and chatted with her mother.

She soon became visibly plump and this troubled her stepmother. 'Why is Man Vang becoming so plump even when I am not giving her anything to eat? And why does she leave the house every evening?' she thought to herself. She went to Man Vang's father and threatened that unless he killed whoever was providing food for Man Vang, she would leave him.

So, he secretly followed Man Vang the next evening and demanded that she call out to whoever was giving her the food. Man Vang desperately tried to plead with her father but he wouldn't hear it.

"Call it now or I'll stab you with my spear," he threatened and displayed his spear. Man Vang began to weep again but she hesitantly did as she was told. "Mother, Mother! Father is threatening to kill me if you don't..." her father interrupted by raising his spear up. "Call her the way you usually do! If she knows I am here, she won't come out!"

Realizing she had no way to escape, Man Vang pitifully called to her mother. As soon as the python was in sight and in reach, Man Vang's father raised his spear to stab the creature. But Man Vang could not stand the thought of her father murdering her own mother. So, she cried out, "Mother! Look out!"

The python heard her warning and immediately slithered back in the water. "You idiot! Call it again or I will kill the both of you!" roared her father. Again, Man Vang called to her mother. For the second time, the python came slithering out of the water.

Man Vang's father raised his spear to stab the python once more, but again, Man Vang shouted, "Mother! Look out!" Immediately, the python slithered back into the water. "Call that dreaded woman back out! This time, if you interfere, I will most certainly kill you both!"

Knowing that her father was now very serious, Man Vang called her mother back out as she wept. As soon as the python was in reach, Man Vang's father plunged his spear down and stabbed it. He dragged his daughter and the dead body of his deceased wife back home. When her stepmother saw it, she couldn't help but grin malevolently. Then, she ordered poor Man Vang to cook the python, although she was already traumatized enough.

While cooking, Man Vang sobbed and sobbed. "Mother, Mother, which part of you is ready to be eaten now?" she asked. "My daughter, my daughter, my tail is ready," came the reply. After a little while, Man Vang repeated her question. "Mother, Mother, which part of you is ready to be eaten now?" she said. "My daughter, my daughter, my stomach is ready," came the reply. After a little while, Man Vang repeated her question again. "Mother, Mother, which part of you is ready to be eaten now?" she said. "My daughter, my daughter, my head is ready," said her mother.

Before Man Vang could bring her to the table, her mother, the python spoke. "My daughter, do not eat my meat under any circumstance. Once they have finished eating me, gather my bones, wrap them with a white cloth, and bury them by the river. In three days, come to my grave and bring *changvut dil sarih* (seven loaves of rice cakes)," she instructed.

Heartbroken, Man Vang prepared her mother's meat for her stepmother, her stepsister, and her father. They did not even invite her to eat with them, not that she wanted to. She watched them grievously as they consumed her mother's meat.

As Man Vang gathered the bones of her mother, she noticed that there were still bits of meat clinging to the bones. Because her mother had told her not to eat, Man Vang dropped the bits of meat in a small hole in the house. A rooster spotted the meat, and he flapped his wings around and crowed.

"*Ti-ta-di-kawk! Ti-ta-di-kawk!* Man Vang is dropping bits of meat! Man Vang is dropping bits of meat!" he crowed vociferously. Man Vang's father was furious and pointed his finger at her accusingly. "Why are you dropping meat into the holes, Man Vang?" he demanded angrily.

Man Vang shook her head in denial. "No, no, Father! The rooster is lying; I did not throw anything in the opening!" she said. As soon as her father went back inside the house, Man Vang slipped away and ran to the river and buried her mother's bones dolefully.

Three days later, she returned to the grave bringing *changvut dil sarih*, as her mother had told her to do. The minute she set the loaves down, stunning pieces of jewelry and accessories appeared before her, along with amazingly beautiful garments. They were made of fine silk and felt like the softest of velvets.

Man Vang put the garments on and wore some of the jewelry. But she made sure to take the jewelry off as soon as she arrived home. She was afraid that her stepmother and stepsister would accuse her of stealing and then take them away from her. When they saw her in her lovely new dress, they were even more envious. They made fun of her and called it ugly, but soon demanded that she share her dress with Man Bo.

"Share it with your sister right now, or we'll take it away from you," said her stepmother sternly. So, Man Vang took her dress off and gave it to Man Bo. As soon as Man Bo wore it, the dress turned into a hideous, muddy dress with rags and rips and dirt on it. But as soon as Man Vang put it back on, it magically transformed into the beautiful dress it once was.

Near their village, there lived a powerful chief who had a handsome young son named A Lal. A Lal's father had been trying to find a wife for his son, and encouraged him to visit Man Vang's village. When A Lal saw Man Vang, he instantly fell in love.

He went back to his village and told his father to ask Man Vang's parents for her hand in marriage. Man Bo's mother was quite furious that Man Vang would be getting married first, especially to such a high-ranking man. Fearing that she might leave him, Man Vang's father secretly went to A Lal and made a deal with him.

"Please, ask us for Man Bo's hand instead of Man Vang's. It will be as if you are marrying her, but you will actually take Man Vang as your bride." A Lal agreed to it and asked for Man Bo's hand in marriage. Both Man Bo and her mother were ecstatic.

Man Bo haughtily strutted across town and went to her friends, boasting that she would marry the son of a chief. "Now that I am going to be married, provide me with all the things that I need!" she jokingly demanded from her friends.

When the time came to leave, Man Vang was asked to accompany Man Bo to A Lal's village. She did as she was told, but before they reached the village, A Lal's servants suddenly pushed Man Bo over to the side of the road and then left the humiliated Man Bo all by herself. Then they continued on with Man Vang to A Lal's village where the two were married.

Man Bo had trudged back to their village with her scarred face wet with tears of humiliation and rage. When Man Bo's mother saw her daughter in such a dreadful condition, she was absolutely livid with Man Vang.

That night, Man Bo and her mother plotted a way to get revenge. "After what she has done to you, my sweet daughter, Man Vang must die!" Man Bo's mother seethed. "We will lie to Man Vang that her father has grown very ill and that she has to come and take care of him. During her visit, we will kill her," she plotted.

She told the plan to Man Vang's father. "This is because of your daughter. You *must* play along with our plan, or else." The man would have turned it down immediately, had it not been for the spell he was under.

After a while, they sent the false news to Man Vang that her father had suddenly taken ill. Without knowing their evil plot, Man Vang immediately rushed back to her village to tend to her father.

During dinner one night, her stepmother pretended to accidentally drop her spoon in a hole on the floor and told Man Vang to pick it up. While Man Vang went under the house to pick up the spoon, Man Bo suddenly poured a whole cauldron full of boiling water over her. Man Vang let out a painful shriek for just a slight moment but then died.

Following her death, her stepmother and Man Bo cut off Man Vang's breasts and hung them on a tall tree just on the outskirts of their village. They dressed Man Bo up as Man Vang again and she went to A Lal's village.

A Lal and his servants were, of course, very suspicious of Man Bo. However, there was nothing they could do. To test her, A Lal told her to weave a nice shawl for him. Man Vang was an expert weaver and her weaving always proved to be magnificent.

Man Bo was not a weaver at all. So, she pretended to work with the loom. "*Ka-ṭhung, ka-ṭhung.*," She made the weaving sound although she was not actually weaving anything.

A few days later, a magical raven came upon Man Vang's breasts and brought them back to his nest. Then, he cast a spell on them to transform them back into Man Vang. The raven insisted that she babysit his children in return for giving her life again. While taking tender care of the little ravens, Man Vang would lull them to sleep by singing a song she made up on her own:

> "*A hlan ah cun, a hlan ah cun,*
> *A Lal nupi ka rak si.*
> *A tu ah cun ka pu langak pa fa ka um ai.*"

Loose English Translation:
"Long ago, long ago,
I was once A Lal's wife
But now I look after my uncle the raven's children."

One day, A Lal's servants were strolling in the same woods where Man Vang lived and heard her melodious singing. "Hey, listen to that," they told each other. The servants stayed silent and listened to Man Vang's beautiful voice. The servants rushed back to the village and informed A Lal about their encounter.

A Lal immediately commanded that they bring his beloved wife back to him. Obediently, they went back and called to the raven. The servants began to plead for Man Vang's return. "You may take her back *if* you agree to give me a basketful of charcoal and a spoonful of insects."

A Lal's servants went back to the village and gathered a basketful of charcoal and a spoonful of insects, as the raven wanted. They ran back to the forest and gave the raven the things they had gathered. Then, the raven allowed Man Vang to go with the servants.

Back in the village, Man Vang was greeted by happy villagers. The next day, A Lal announced that the entire village, and their neighboring villages, would all celebrate Man Vang's return. Then, A Lal organized a *khuangcawi puai* (a Chin ceremonial feast, honoring high-ranking women).

Man Bo and her mother received news of the feast and they were both extremely angry. "We tried killing her but she miraculously survived!" they said. "Man Vang has put us through too much. Our lives are miserable because of her. We must take revenge," they concluded.

They dressed Man Bo up in Man Vang's clothes again, and with the help of the witch's magic, Man Bo assumed the face of Man Vang. Man Vang's father had died of old age so he could not be part of their evil scheme. They went to the feast and the villagers all noticed that there were two of Man Vang.

They were all very perplexed. "Who is Man Vang and who is the imposter?" they asked one another. Out of A Lal's servants, there was one particular servant who was rather clever. "Sire, we shall make two swords; one that will be a real sword that we cover in charcoal, and the other will be a fake but shining wooden sword. We will let the two Man Vang's choose their sword and they will duel. Whoever wins the duel is the true Man Vang, and we shall honor her in the *khuangcawi puai.*"

So, the next day, A Lal announced that the two stepsisters would duel in order to find out who was the real Man Vang. Both stepsisters knew who was who but the villagers needed the proof. The servants gave the stepsisters nice food to eat and refreshing water to drink.

When it was time to duel, the servants dressed Man Bo in a lovely dress, both beautiful and suited for fighting. Man Vang chose the real sword that was charcoal-covered, and Man Bo chose the fake sword that was covered with shiny material.

As soon as the duel began, Man Vang sneered and shouted, "Strike me, strike me, Man Bo! May your sword rebound!" (in Chin, *"Man Bo, ka tu, ka tu! Cholkung!"*) With a scream of fury, Man Bo savagely struck Man Vang. She could not harm her, however.

Then, when it was Man Vang's turn to strike, Man Bo sneered with twice the callous and shouted, "Strike me, strike me, Man Vang! May your sword shatter!" (in Chin, *"Man Vang, ka tu, ka tu! Tlam suai!"*) In the blink of an eye, Man Vang brought her sword down upon her stepsister and cut her in half.

A Lal kissed and embraced Man Vang for winning the duel. They celebrated her victory and they honored her in the *khuangcawi puai.*

A Lal was very angry with Man Bo's mother for tricking him. So, he ordered his servants to cut up the remains of Man Bo, pickle her, and send her back to her mother in an earthen jar.

"Man Bo's husband has gifted you with pickled meat," A Lal's servants said when they dropped it off. Man Bo's mother was very eager and excited to open the lid. At dinner, her mother opened it up and scooped a piece of pickled meat. The second time, though, she scooped up Man Bo's thumb.

"Why, it looks just like my daughter's thumb," she murmured. The wife scooped up another piece and examined it. "Why, it looks just like my daughter's big toe!" she began to grow fretful. Finally, Man Bo's mother scooped up one last piece. This time, she screamed when she saw it was Man Bo's severed head! She began to sob.

"Oh, they have slaughtered my beautiful daughter and tricked us into eating her very flesh!" she shrieked. She furiously wept and wept and decided to avenge her daughter.

Hurriedly, the witch ran to A Lal's village to confront him, but little did she know that A Lal's servants had been ordered to kill her if they saw her.

When they saw the witch running towards them, they shot at her with their bows and arrows. She managed to escape and run up the stairs but tripped and fell backwards, crushing many bones. Still alive, but in great pain, Man Bo's mother desperately clawed at the stairs, but before she could make it all the way up, a massive and deadly guard dog caught and ripped her to shreds before killing her. Instead of properly burying her, they threw her disfigured body away in the wastelands.

Man Vang and A Lal then lived happily ever after.

Ral Dawn and Tum Sing

Ral Dawn and Tum Sing is the story of two young lovers who meet because of a beautiful fruit. An unfortunate mistake causes Tum Sing to be killed and replaced by an ugly old witch. Ral Dawn soon discovers the truth about his wife. But all is not lost. She miraculously returns to life and the couple live happily together for a long time. However, a sudden twist and a broken promise turn the blissful picture to a tragic one.

Generations ago, there lived a couple who had one son. They named him Ral Dawn. He was a very handsome and hard-working fellow. Since the time when he was young, Ral Dawn would follow his parents to the fields in order to help them with their work.

One day, Ral Dawn and his father went to the field. While working, Ral Dawn spotted a beautiful fruit. Never had he seen such a wonderful thing, so he plucked it and displayed it for his father to see and admire.

"Look, father! Have you ever seen such a gorgeous fruit? I wonder if there is a woman on earth who can challenge the beauty of this fruit," he said with immense admiration. His father agreed that it was a beautiful fruit, but he said that he had heard from village talk of a young woman who was more beautiful than the richest and finest of princesses.

"They call her Tum Sing, and she is said to have glorious beauty. Perhaps she can match your fruit." After hearing this, Ral Dawn became very desperate to see Tum Sing's face. He told his parents that he could not go without seeing and marrying this Tum Sing, and set off with his fruit.

Only after travelling a few miles, he came across the village of a young woman who wove *biarpi* (a type of loincloth). He walked over to her, and as soon as the woman saw him she asked, "Where are you going? What are you going to do?"

"I am going to find and marry Tum Sing," Ral Dawn answered. The young woman smiled delightedly and exclaimed, "I am Tum Sing! Marry me!" As mentioned before, Ral Dawn was a fine-looking fellow who was young and handsome.

Ral Dawn looked at her and then pulled out his fruit. He compared them and concluded that she was not Tum Sing, for the fruit was more beautiful than her. He went on until he came across the village of a woman who made cloaks. He walked over to her, and as soon as the woman saw him she asked, "Where are you going? What are you going to do?"

"I am going to find and marry Tum Sing," Ral Dawn answered. The young woman then exclaimed, "I am Tum Sing! Marry me!" Ral Dawn looked at her and then pulled out his fruit. He compared them and concluded that she was not Tum Sing, for the fruit was more beautiful than her.

He went on until he came across the village of a woman who made *conlo* (a type of traditional shawl worn by men). He walked over to her, and as soon as the woman saw him she asked, "Where are you going? What are you going to do?"

"I am going to find and marry Tum Sing," Ral Dawn answered. The young woman then exclaimed, "I am Tum Sing! Marry me!" Ral Dawn looked at her and then pulled out his fruit. He compared them and concluded that she was not Tum Sing, for the fruit was more beautiful than her.

He went on until he finally came across Tum Sing's village. He went to the nearest young woman he saw, which so happened to be Tum Sing. She was in the middle of weaving *cawngnak* (a piece of traditional Chin clothing). Tum Sing was so beautiful, people often said she was as beautiful as *Lasi* (fairies, or little people in Chin mythology; they are said to be very beautiful).

Tum Sing had elegant, long, raven-black hair and her skin was smooth and golden. Her hands were soft and her fingers were dainty, as were her toes. Unhurriedly, Tum Sing looked up from her weaving, which was almost as beautiful as her, and asked in a fragrant voice, "Hello there. Where are you going? What are you going to do?"

"I am going to find and marry Tum Sing," Ral Dawn answered. Tum Sing smiled kindly and replied with a voice almost amused, "Alright, you go ahead and marry her. Good luck with that." Ral Dawn turned around and was about to leave, when he realized just how beautiful she was.

Slowly, he pulled out his pretty fruit and glanced at the two. In just a couple of heartbeats, Ral Dawn decided that Tum Sing was ten times more beautiful than his fruit. Ral Dawn fell in love with her immediately. As much as she was trying to hide it, Tum Sing liked him back, for he was a handsome young man. The two loved each other so much that it is almost impossible to describe in words.

Tum Sing told Ral Dawn that her parents would be back from working in the fields very soon. "Now, I will give you some *zuhui* (porridge with alcohol in it) and *zureu* (alcohol). My parents will ask you if I had fed you anything. You are to say 'No, she did not.'"

With that, Tum Sing began to make the best *zuhui* and *zureu* for Ral Dawn. As Tum Sing had said, her parents did return from the fields not long after. Tum Sing did not announce the proposal or marriage to her parents in fear that they would not let her marry. Instead, she told them that Ral Dawn was a friend.

Her parents then began to ask the slightly drunk Ral Dawn about his life. "Ah, Ral Dawn, did our daughter give you any *zuhui* and *zureu* to eat and drink?" they asked. Ral Dawn, although drunk, knew it was not a good idea to go against the young maiden's word, so he replied with, "No, she did not."

"Oh, Tum Sing, why did you not prepare any of it for our guest? Quickly, fix some for this gentleman," they shooed their daughter. While Tum Sing prepared the second round of *zuhui* and *zureu*, she glanced at Ral Dawn with a pleasant smile. She placed the *zuhui* and *zureu* in front of Ral Dawn. He tried to consume them, but he was too drunk to do so.

Ral Dawn spent the night in their house, and in the morning, after Tum Sing's parents went out in the fields again, he and Tum Sing secretly ran away together. As Tum Sing's unknowing parents worked, a little bird flew to them and began to chirp.

"Mother and Father of Tum Sing, you say you love your daughter but Ral Dawn has now taken her far away, over nine hills, ten hills," it chirped. At first, neither parent heard what the little bird was saying, but soon, Tum Sing's mother did. "My love, listen to that! The little bird says, 'Mother and Father of Tum Sing, you say you love your daughter but Ral Dawn has now taken her far away, over nine hills, ten hills.'"

Tum Sing's father shook his head. "Ah, you're just nagging me because you don't want to do your work. Keep quiet and work," he grumbled.

Meanwhile, Ral Dawn and Tum Sing were still travelling to Ral Dawn's village. Halfway there, they came across a well belonging to *Pinu* (ugly, witch-like demons in Chin mythology). All of a sudden, Tum Sing suddenly cried out in distress.

"Oh no! I forgot to close the lid to my silver jewelry box!" Tum Sing began to cry, because the jewelry in the box was very expensive and precious. With nobody to guard the house, somebody could easily steal it. "Now, now, please don't cry. I will go and grab the box for you. You just stay here. Climb that tree and keep hidden. If you see any strangers, don't interact with them," Ral Dawn said.

Tum Sing nodded and climbed up a big and tall tree. She curled herself up so that she was hidden within the leaves to wait for Ral Dawn. At that moment, a *Pinu* suddenly appeared to collect water from the well.

As she collected the water, she saw Tum Sing's beautiful reflection, looking down at her. Thinking it was her own reflection, she grinned and said, "They call me a *Pinu*; they call me an ugly hag! Why, I am so beautiful!" The *Pinu* danced and skipped around in joy. After she finished collecting the water, she strutted away in a satisfied and merry manner.

Soon, another *Pinu* came along, and another and another. They all looked at themselves in the water and saw Tum Sing's gorgeous reflection. Like the *Pinu* before all of them, they believed that it was their own reflection, and they all bragged conceitedly before skipping contentedly away.

After they had all gone away, one more *Pinu* came to the well to collect some water. She looked at herself, and like all the others, she thought Tum Sing's reflection was her own reflection. Before she had a chance to say anything, however, the very impatient and angry Tum Sing interrupted her. She'd had to witness several unpleasant witches mistake her beautiful face for theirs, and she could no longer hold the anger and impatience inside.

"That is *my* reflection, you ugly *Pinu!*" she barked from the tree. Tum Sing instantly shielded her mouth and tried to conceal herself in the tree again, but it was too late. The *Pinu* had already spotted her. She climbed up the tree abnormally fast, as if she were a squirrel, and devoured Tum Sing.

A single drop of Tum Sing's blood fell on the forest floor and immediately a magnificent banyan tree grew. A stunning fruit grew from the tree, one even more beautiful than the one Ral Dawn had found before. Paying no interest to this, the *Pinu* dressed herself in Tum Sing's clothing and waited for Ral Dawn to return from his task.

When Ral Dawn returned, he instantaneously noticed that the imposter looked nothing like Tum Sing. However, she was still in the tree, and she was wearing the same clothes, so there was nothing he could really do.

"Well, come on, then. Let us continue," he said with suspicion in his voice. Before they left, Ral Dawn noticed the tree and the beautiful fruit. He plucked it, put it in his little bag, and they set off once more. The *Pinu* followed Ral Dawn obediently, and he noticed that some of her fingers were smaller and some larger than each other.

"Tum Sing, why are your fingers in such a disfigured shape?" he asked. The Pinu replied, "While you were away, I was daydreaming so much about how much we would embrace each other, that they came to look like this."

"Tum Sing, why are your arms uneven? One is higher up than the other," Ral Dawn said. "While you were away, I was daydreaming so much about how you would massage my poor fingers that they came to be like this," the *Pinu* said. "Tum Sing, why are your legs uneven? One is higher up than the other," Ral Dawn said. The Pinu replied, "While you were away, I was daydreaming so much about when we would reach your village that they came to be like this."

Now that she had explained everything, Ral Dawn could no longer think of any other questions to test her with. So, he decided there was nothing he could do and it would be rude to accuse her of being an imposter. He kept silent the rest of the way.

In a few hours, they arrived at Ral Dawn's village. When they arrived at his house, Ral Dawn hung the fruit he had carried in a little bag on the corner wall.

One day, Ral Dawn and Tum Sing's pretender went to the field to complete some work. Before they returned home, however, the food, water, and fire were already prepared for them. As anybody else would be, Ral Dawn was very surprised. Nobody else was in the house and they had gone out to the fields, so who could have done this?

Ral Dawn went to his next-door neighbor, a widow, and asked whether she had made the food for them. "Yes, I did," she replied, although she really did not. "Well, then, come and join us for dinner!" Ral Dawn invited her. This strange thing happened every day when both Ral Dawn and his wife's imposter went out. Soon, Ral Dawn realized that it wasn't his neighbor the widow that was doing this. He wanted to know who was.

So, one day, Ral Dawn made the *Pinu* go the field by herself. He stayed at home and hid in order to find out who was responsible for this. When it was evening, the little bag that carried the fruit Ral Dawn had brought home, opened up, and out crawled his beautiful wife, Tum Sing! She went over to the kitchen and began to cook the food for them.

Quietly, Ral Dawn sneaked up on Tum Sing and grabbed her without giving her a chance to cry out. "Let me go!" she yelled. "Let you go? Let you go? You are my wife! Why would I let you go?" He held onto Tum Sing even tighter in fear that she might slip away from him.

Finally, Tum Sing stopped struggling. "All right! Let me go and I will stay with you. I won't leave you," she promised. However, Ral Dawn was very cautious and did not believe her. He remained holding onto her. The two struggled for a little bit more, and eventually, Ral Dawn let go, for he was exhausted.

As she had promised, Tum Sing did not leave again. Instead, she and Ral Dawn chatted for a bit and began to eat the food she had made. When both Ral Dawn and Tum Sing had finished eating their food, they prepared a huge pot-full of boiling water. Afterwards, the couple slipped into the *chakchang* (a typical bed in a traditional Chin house situated by a fireplace), and went to bed.

The *Pinu* returned home near nightfall drenched from head to toe with rain water, for it was raining heavily. She left the firewood she had collected outside. When she went inside, she caught sight of the lovers in bed, but assumed they were just brother and sister hugging each other.

Ral Dawn then got up from the *chakchang* and pretended to accidentally drop a comb in the small opening in the floor. He told the *Pinu* to pick it up and as she did, Ral Dawn poured the boiling water over her. The *Pinu* screamed in terrifying agony, but very speedily perished.

After she died, Ral Dawn told Tum Sing she was free to do whatever she wanted with the body of the *Pinu*, so she pummeled it again and again in her mortar. Once she was quite contented, she threw the remains in the corner of the garden. From where she threw the remains away, an *anhling* (a kind of green vegetable) plant grew.

When she saw the *anhling* plant, Tum Sing collected it and used it to make *buti* (traditional Chin soup; porridge). As she cooked, the *buti* pot began to boil and made an irritating sound. "*Porh, porh, kek, kek,*" it said. (It was like the pot was saying "Let the *buti* grow and pop." It was taunting Tum Sing). Tum Sing knew that it was the *Pinu* trying to mock her, so she angrily threw the *buti* out into the garden again.

From where she threw the *buti* away, a tall banana plant grew. The banana plant was much longer than other plants and it stood out above the rest.

One day, Ral Dawn had to go on a trip. Before leaving, he warned Tum Sing not to bite the tallest banana plant without mentioning why. "I promise not to bite the banana plant, my love," Tum Sing pledged. The couple kissed each other goodbye and Ral Dawn set off.

Just a few days after Ral Dawn left, Tum Sing decided to go to the field to work while her husband was away. She looked for something to wrap her lunch in but there was nothing to use. Tum Sing went to her neighbors and asked if they had anything she could use. But that was in vain.

Hence, she decided to use the banana leaves from her garden. Of course, she picked the longest one, as it would be the best one to wrap her lunch. Tum Sing tried to pull it but she could not no matter how hard she pulled.

Forgetting what she had promised to Ral Dawn, she decided to grind the stem with her teeth so it would come off. As soon as she bit into it, her tongue was cut off! Tum Sing instantly dropped to the ground and died.

A few days later, Ral Dawn returned from his trip. The villagers told him about his wife's death and Ral Dawn was stricken with grief. He wanted to visit her grave very much but Ral Dawn had no clue where they had buried his love.

Luckily, a group of young boys who had been hunting for birds went up to him and told him where she had been buried. Ral Dawn went to the grave and dug out the soil. He lay down next to the coffin and took out his hairpin. With the sharp end pointing towards him, Ral Dawn pierced himself in the chest. Ral Dawn joined his beautiful love Tum Sing in death.

Kum Ṭung and Tlai Tleng

Kum Ṭung and Tlai Tleng are two brothers that have been completely different from each other since the day they were born. Kum Ṭung is callous and short-tempered whereas his younger brother Tlai Tleng is kindhearted and patient. After cheating in a competition to marry a beautiful young woman named Thai Hliang, Kum Ṭung goes on a long journey, encountering and neglecting many different animals in need. His plan to marry Thai Hliang are crushed, however, leaving her to be successfully taken by his brother, who makes sure to avoid the same mistakes as his brother.

Once upon a time, there lived two brothers called Kum Ṭung and Tlai Tleng. From the time they were young, the two of them often went into the woods to hunt for birds. When they grew up, both brothers turned into fine young men.

Ever since they were little, they were rather different from each other. Kum Ṭung, the older, was short-tempered and rude. He was always very selfish and took no notice of other people's problems. Tlai Tleng, the younger, was kind and patient. He was always willing to help others and he was always fair.

One day, the brothers decided to do a slingshot competition. Whoever won the competition would marry Thai Hliang, a beautiful young woman from a nearby village. They decided to use an egg as their target for the competition.

First, the elder brother, Kum Ṭung swung his slingshot at the egg but he missed it. Then, it was Tlai Tleng's turn. He swung his slingshot, but contrary to his brother, he managed to hit it. Tlai Tleng let out a cheer and jumped in the air in ecstasy.

"I will marry Thai Hliang!" he exclaimed happily. However, his older brother was bitter that Tlai Tleng had won. He refused to allow this. "You are the younger one! How dare you say you will be the one to marry Thai Hliang!" argued Kum Ṭung and brutally beat his brother. Tlai Tleng wept miserably and ran back home to their mother.

"Mother, my brother told me that we would compete in a slingshot competition and whoever won would get to marry Thai Hliang. I won but he beat me and said I couldn't marry her because I was younger!" Tlai Tleng reported to his mother.

"Well, what he said was true! You are the younger brother, after all. How could you marry Thai Hliang?" she scolded. Seeing his mother would not support him, the heartbroken Tlai Tleng went to his aunt, who was always willing to help him out.

"Why are you crying? Why are you so sad?" asked his aunt when he arrived. "Aunty, my brother told me that we would compete in a slingshot competition and whoever won would get to marry Thai Hliang. I won but he beat me and said

I couldn't marry her because I was younger! I told my mother but she just scolded me." His aunt listened patiently to him and comforted him. "Ah, don't be sad, my son. You will be the one who marries Thai Hliang."

Meanwhile, Kum Ṭung was getting ready to set off to marry Thai Hliang. On his way, he came across a flock of thirsty sparrows. They were busily searching for good, clean water in a muddy marsh.

"Kum Ṭung, we are very thirsty. Please spare some of the water you have with you!" they pleaded. "Are you the ones who have been eating our grains in the field?" he shouted and chased them with rocks. The sparrows were so surprised and frightened so they all flew away. As they flew away, they all chirped, "You won't marry Thai Hliang!"

He ignored them and continued on. As he approached a brook, he spotted a squirrel that was trapped. "Kum Ṭung, please set me free from this trap!" pleaded the squirrel. "I'm on my way to marry Thai Hliang and you're being a pest. Don't bother me. Aren't you the one who eats our corn all the time?" he said and tightened the trap even more. As he walked away, the squirrel squeaked, "You won't marry Thai Hliang!"

Again, he ignored the squirrel and continued on. Soon, he came across a family of monkeys. The children looked very hungry but there was no good food around. "Kum Ṭung, please share us your loaf of bread. My children are very hungry," pleaded the mother monkey.

"How shameful of you! Aren't you the ones who eat our corn?" he said and chased the family all around. As he walked away, the monkeys yelled, "You won't marry Thai Hliang!" He ignored the monkeys and continued on.

He walked on until he met a big snake. "Kum Ṭung, please give me some of your leftover food," pleaded the snake. "Aren't you the one who bites people?" he said and struck the snake's head with a stick. He slithered away, frightened. As Kum Ṭung walked away, the snake hissed, "you won't marry Thai Hliang!"

Again, he ignored the snake and continued on. He went on until he saw a young woman collecting water from a brook. "Sir, please hold onto my water jar," she requested. "You should be ashamed! I'm on my way to marry Thai Hliang, a beautiful goddess, and you are slowing me down! I will be late!" he said and pushed her water jar.

He continued on and finally arrived at Thai Hliang's house. Kum Ṭung invited himself into the house and patiently waited for Thai Hliang to appear.

Soon, Thai Hliang, too, arrived home. What the unfortunate Kum Ṭung did not know was that the young woman he had met by the brook was none other than Thai Hliang! When she arrived, she saw Kum Ṭung sitting on her porch.

The minute she saw him, she knew he was the rude young man who had knocked over her water jar. Despite this, Thai Hliang put on a pleasant face and conversed with him nicely. Kum Ṭung, too, immediately recognized her, and he was so embarrassed that he couldn't properly speak to her.

Thai Hliang made him some *zuhui* (porridge with alcohol in it) and served it to him. In a short while, her parents came home from working in the field. They acknowledged Kum Ṭung but didn't say much to him.

The next day Thai Hliang's father questioned Kum Ṭung. "Which side of our house is the width and which side is the length?" he said. That was an odd question and Kum Ṭung was stumped. He did not know how to answer. So, taking a wild guess, he answered. "This side is the width and that side is the length," he pointed to different sides of the house.

"Which side of our wood mortar is the bottom and which side is the top?" Thai Hliang's father asked him another question. Again, Kum Ṭung did not know the answer, so he took another wild guess. "This side is the bottom and this side is the top," he pointed to two different sides of the mortar.

Another night passed and Thai Hliang's father gave Kum Ṭung a variety of tests that made absolutely no sense. Kum Ṭung was always very confused and he could never complete them in the correct way. He had to lie his way out of some of the tests.

In the end, Thai Hliang's father agreed to give his daughter to Kum Ṭung, not because he approved of him, but because it was a part of the test. He was not so willing to let his daughter go so easily. "Tomorrow, you may bring my daughter home with you," he announced. Thus, the next morning, Kum Ṭung and Thai Hliang prepared lunch for the journey and set off.

They needed to pluck a banana leaf to wrap their lunch, but Kum Ṭung did not pick a good, firm leaf. The leaf he picked was tattered and torn. Even though they packed much lunch, most of it could not fit because the leaf was in such a bad condition.

After Thai Hliang's parents decided she and Kum Ṭung had gone a long way, they went to their faithful big dogs, and unleashed them to chase after their daughter and the young man. Thai Hliang's parents wanted to make sure Kum Ṭung would be prepared for the dogs. Aware that the dogs had been sent after them from the barking in the distance, Kum Ṭung and Thai Hliang left some of their lunch on the ground for the dogs to get distracted by.

The dogs soon came across the food and stopped to eat it. While they ate it, Kum Ṭung and Thai Hliang ran farther away. However, the dogs quickly consumed the food and continued to chase after them. They eventually caught up and killed Kum Ṭung and escorted Thai Hliang back to her home.

Back in Kum Ṭung's village, Tlai Tleng's thoughts were busy wondering about this older brother. 'How come my older brother has not returned yet? What could have happened?' He decided to go and see what his brother was doing at Thai Hliang's house. He packed a lot of food for the journey and set off.

As he approached a brook, he spotted a squirrel that was trapped. "Tlai Tleng, please set me free from this trap!' pleaded the squirrel. The kindhearted Tlai Tleng paused his journey to help the little squirrel. He bid him farewell and continued on with his journey. Before he walked away, the squirrel squeaked, "You will marry Thai Hliang!"

Soon, he came across a flock of thirsty sparrows. They were still busily searching for good, clean water in a now dry brook.

"Tlai Tleng, we are very thirsty. Please dig up some water for us!" they pleaded. Pausing his journey, the kindhearted Tlai Tleng dug up some water from the brook. He bid them farewell and continued on with his journey. Before he walked away, the sparrows chirped, "You will marry Thai Hliang!"

A little while later, he came across a family of hungry monkeys. They were desperately eating some dirt because they were so starved.

"Tlai Tleng, we are all very hungry. Please lend us some of your *vaireu* (a type of Chin food made out of fried corn)!" they pleaded. Pausing his journey, the kindhearted Tlai Tleng lent them some of his *vaireu*. He bid them farewell and continued on with his journey. Before he walked away, the monkeys yelled, "You will marry Thai Hliang!"

Tlai Tleng kept on going until he eventually came across a big snake. "Tlai Tleng, I am very hungry. Please give me some of your journey food!" he pleaded. Pausing his journey, the kindhearted Tlai Tleng lent him some of his journey food. He bid him farewell and continued on with his journey. Before he walked away, the snake hissed, "You will marry Thai Hliang!"

Just before arriving at Thai Hliang's village, Tlai Tleng spotted a young woman collecting water from a well. "Sir, please hold onto my basket," she requested. Pausing his journey, the kindhearted Tlai Tleng held onto her basket.

The two of them went into the village together and Tlai Tleng found out that the young woman was none other than Thai Hliang! As soon as they entered the house, Thai Hliang served him a banana and some *zuhui*.

As he ate, Thai Hliang told Tlai Tleng, "When my parents return from the field, my father will ask you a variety of odd questions. I will tell you the answers to all of them." She told him all the answers to her father's questions. "You must remember all of this if you wish to marry me and survive," she added when finished.

In the evening, Thai Hliang's parents returned from the field. They acknowledged Tlai Tleng but didn't say much to him.

The next day, Thai Hliang's father gave Tlai Tleng a variety of questions, as Thai Hliang had forewarned. The questions were the same as the ones Thai Hliang's father had asked Kum Ṭung. Thanks to the help of Thai Hliang, though, Tlai Tleng managed to answer each of the questions correctly.

Thai Hliang's father also gave him a variety of tests, like he did with Kum Ṭung. Thai Hliang's instructions always lingered in Tlai Tleng's mind and helped him pass the tests. It wasn't only Thai Hliang's instructions that helped him, the animals he had helped on his journey helped him out, as well.

For example, one day, Thai Hliang's father ordered Tlai Tleng to pick up each and every one of the seeds he had dropped all around the field the night before. He went to the flock of sparrows for help and they all willingly picked the seeds up for him.

Seeing that he could complete all of the impossible tasks they had set up for him, Thai Hliang's parents were very surprised and impressed. Especially her father. He decided that he was a very good choice for his daughter.

So, one day, Thai Hliang's father went to Tlai Tleng and gave him his consent to marry his daughter. "Tomorrow, you may bring my daughter home with you," he announced. The next day, they packed an assortment of foods, including many bones, and set off to head back to Tlai Tleng's village.

Unlike his brother, Tlai Tleng had picked, with the help of the big snake, a nice, firm, and fresh banana leaf to wrap their lunch in. They could fit all the foods they had packed inside.

Although Thai Hliang's parents liked Tlai Tleng very much, they were not so willing to give him or anyone their daughter. So, after they decided they had gone a long way, they unleashed their big dogs after them again.

Tlai Tleng and Thai Hliang knew the dogs were coming so they left behind a handful of food and bones, not once, not twice, but throughout their entire journey. In the end, the dogs could not catch up to them because they had been so distracted with the food.

They arrived safely back at Tlai Tleng's village and were quickly married. Later, Thai Hliang gave birth to five handsome sons.

Alternate Ending:

Tlai Tleng and Thai Hlang's sons grew up to be well-rounded young men. They were all very clever and quick-witted. One day, the brothers decided they wanted to meet their maternal grandparents. Their parents tried to warn them not to, in fear that they might be killed.

However, all of the brothers were very stubborn, they refused to listen and went to Thai Hliang's old village. Their grandfather did not like them very much, for they were always getting into mischief.

One day, the brothers told their grandfather, "We are going to feed the chickens." They went into the chicken coop but were greeted with a bunch of *arṭau* (small, wild chickens). "Grandfather, your chickens look like *arṭau*!" they exclaimed.

"We are *arṭau*!" The chickens flapped their wings as they remembered their past and flew into the woods. Later that day, the brothers told their grandfather, "We are going to feed the dogs." They went to the dogs but were greeted with a bunch of foxes. "Grandfather, your big dogs look like foxes!" they exclaimed.

"We are foxes!" the dogs barked as they remembered their past and ran into the woods. In the evening, the brothers told their grandfather, "We are going to feed the pigs." They went to the pig pen but were greeted with a bunch of wild boars. "Grandfather, your pigs look like wild boar!" they exclaimed.

"We are wild boars!" the pigs squealed as they remembered their past and ran into the woods. Thai Hliang's father grew very angry. 'These boys have rid me of all my animals! I will surely kill them all!' he thought furiously.

The next day, their grandfather told the brothers to follow him to the field. After working for a bit, he led them under a big tree, which he had secretly cut to make it loose earlier, and sat down to eat lunch with them.

Suddenly, the big tree began to fall! The youngest brother noticed just in time and shouted, "Look out!" His brothers moved out of the way just as the big tree came crashing down right on their grandfather.

They went back to the house to journey back to their village, but were surprised when they no longer saw it. This was because, although nobody had known before, ther grandparents were demons. They had cast a spell on their animals to make them think they were chickens, dogs, and pigs. That is why they had given Kum Ṭung and Tlai Tleng impossible tasks. Packing the things that they could, the brothers headed back to their village and never went back to their grandparents' house again.

Zawl Tling and Ngan Bawm

This classic tale is the Chin version of Romeo and Juliet. It follows the story of two young people, Zawl Tling and Ngan Bawm. They are madly in love but cannot be together, for their families are from two different social classes. One dies because of heartbreak and the other ventures to the Underworld so that they can be together again. Just as all seems well, tragedy strikes and the two are cursed to be separated until the end of time.

Once, long ago, there was a little town in the Chin hills. In this little town, there were two families. One family was wealthy and of a high nobility, whereas the other family wasn't as wealthy. They were of a lower-class. The two families each had one child, one a boy, and the other a girl. The girl belonged to the wealthy, upper-class family, and the boy belonged to the poorer, lower-class family.

Both the boy and the girl were very handsome and beautiful. The upper-class family named their pretty daughter Zawl Tling and the other family named their handsome son Ngan Bawm. When both of the children grew up, they fell deeply in love with each other. However, in those days, it was absolutely forbidden for people of different social classes to get married, let alone two families with such a different social gap.

Due to this unjust social norm, Zawl Ting's family did everything in their power to keep the two lovestruck youths separated. As much as the two tried to rebel against their families and be together, it was simply unmanageable. So, the two could not meet and wept grievously every day.

Zawl Tling missed her lover so much that she spent every moment of every single day sobbing her heart out. Soon, she began to grow physically sick from the heartbreak. Poor Zawl Tling was ailing so much! It was too much to bear to be away from her beloved Ngan Bawm.

Ngan Bawm, too, missed Zawl Tling very much. So, one night, he slipped out of the house and dashed to Zawl Tling's house. Zawl Tling's parents weren't present but it was still very risky to enter. There was no way he could get in through a door but luckily, there was a small hole near the corner of the house that led right into Zawl Tling's room. Ngan Bawm would stick his fingers inside the hole and Zawl Tling would kiss his fingers.

Both of them felt much more relieved and Zawl Tling was getting better from her illness. However, her parents soon found out about this, and they were furious. They warned Ngan Bawm not to go even near Zawl Tling's house. Zawl Tling's parents blocked the opening and every other opening they could find in order to prevent Ngan Bawm from coming in.

Again, Zawl Tling fell terribly ill and Ngan Bawm was almost never happy. Her sickness was so deadly that she couldn't even eat. Eventually, Zawl Tling died from the heartbreak and sorrow.

Ngan Bawm tried to attend her funeral, but Zawl Tling's family blocked him. "You are not allowed! Now go away or else we'll kill you!" they threatened menacingly. Ngan Bawm, as badly as he wished to be at his deceased lover's funeral, did as he was told. He went home and sobbed, refusing to be comforted.

When it was time for Zawl Tling's burial, the undertaker and a couple of other gentlemen started to wrap the traditional cloak around Zawl Tling's body, when her body suddenly grew. The cloak didn't fit her anymore. They had never seen anything like this before, so they were in a state of awe and perplexity.

"Quick, get that young man, Ngan Bawm, and tell him to touch her corpse. Maybe that will help," they suggested. Ngan Bawm arrived and sat next to Zawl Tling's corpse and began to sing a sad song.

"*Ka thai Zawl Zawl aw,*
Ka thai Zawl Zawl aw,
Nang lim sianu ah cang aw law la,
Kei lim siapa ah cang aw ning,
Kawm kawm khat ah
Kan khumh ṭi tawn hna seh law,"

Loose English Translation:
"*Oh, my beloved Zawl Zawl,*
Oh, my beloved Zawl Zawl,
Let you become a female Gaur,
Let me become a male Gaur,
Let them put us in the same house," (metaphorically)

As soon as Ngan Bawm finished his beautiful song, he burst into a flood of tears. He kissed her gently, and immediately her body returned to its regular size. The undertaker and the gentlemen were able to wrap her in the cloak. Everyone in the crowd was all awestruck, and nobody said a word. They had just witnessed some sort of magic.

However, when their sense returned, Zawl Tling's parents angrily chased Ngan Bawm away. "Get away! Get away! Now!" they screamed at him. Ngan Bawm ran away, sobbing pitifully. "All right, let's get her body outside so we can bury her," the people said. They lifted the coffin with the lid open and began to walk out of the room, when Zawl Tling's body suddenly grew once more.

They couldn't fit her body through the door, preventing them from burying her. "Quick, get that young man, Ngan Bawm. Maybe he can help like he did before," they suggested. Sorrowfully, Ngan Bawm returned to the burial and repeated his lovely sad song.

"Ka thai Zawl Zawl aw,
Ka thai Zawl Zawl aw,
Vokla nu ah cang aw la,
Vokrial pa ah cang aw ning,
Kawm kawm khat ah
Kan khumh ti tawn hna seh law,"

Loose English Translation:
"Oh, my beloved Zawl Zawl,
Oh, my beloved Zawl Zawl,
Let you become a young female pig,
Let me become a young male pig,
Let them put us in the same house," (metaphorically)

He kissed her gently and once more, Zawl Tling's body returned to its normal size. The people were just as surprised as before, but Zawl Tling's parents didn't care. They chased the poor boy away, cursing him and yelling dangerous threats to him.

"All right, let's get her body into the grave so we can bury her," the people said. They started to prop the coffin into the grave, but for the third time, Zawl Tling's body grew. She wouldn't fit in the grave. "Quick, get that young man, Ngan Bawm. Maybe he can help like he did before," they suggested for the third time. So, Ngan Bawm went back, his heart aching like never before. He sang his sad love song again.

"Ka thai Zawl Zawl aw,
Ka thai Zawl Zawl aw,
Arpi nu ah cang aw la,
Arhli pa ah cang aw ning,
Kawm kawm khat ah
Kan khumh ti tawn hna seh law,"

Loose English Translation:
"Oh, my beloved Zawl Zawl,
Oh, my beloved Zawl Zawl,
Let you become a hen,
Let me become a rooster,
Let us be put in the same house, (metaphorically)

He kissed her gently and once more, Zawl Tling's body returned to its normal size. Zawl Tling was buried, and her parents chased poor Ngan Bawm away.

Every day, Ngan Bawm visited his lover's grave and planted gorgeous flowers of every color and species. Her grave was truly magnificent, thanks to Ngan Bawm. He made sure it was clean and the flowers all stayed fresh and healthy.

Zawl Tling had been watching him from the Underworld, where all the dead went. She was greatly pleased that her lover went through the trouble to do all this. One day, she called to the cat (in Chin, *sazawte*), who in those days was believed to possess special powers.

In those days, it was believed that the spirit of a deceased person could take the form of a cat. Zawl Tling asked, "Please, dear cat, journey to the upper world and pluck me a couple of my lover, Ngan Bawm's pretty flowers. Make sure to go at night so nobody will spot you and try to kill you," she said.

The *sazawte* did as he was told and every night, plucked a couple of flowers to bring back to Zawl Tling. Ngan Bawm noticed that his flowers were being plucked, for fewer and fewer flowers were remaining at the grave. One night, he waited to catch and punish the thief.

Ngan Bawm waited for a long time, and he decided to give up and go back home, when he saw the cat. The cat gingerly leapt to the grave and gently plucked out a handful of flowers. Ngan Bawm ran at him and managed to grab him.

"How dare you? Who gave you the right to steal my flowers? I'll kill you!" he shouted mindlessly at the cat, who was shaking in fear. "Please, kind sir, don't kill me," he pleaded. Ngan Bawm dropped him and drew back in alarm, not expecting the cat to talk back.

"I was sent to grab these flowers by your lover, Zawl Tling. I am from the Underworld," the cat explained. Ngan Bawm was so relieved to hear this, and he went on his knees to beg the cat to take him to the Underworld. "Of course, I would. But the journey is long and dangerous. A puny human like you would get scared and run away," said the cat.

Ngan Bawm shook his head. "No, no. I promise I won't be scared. There's nothing I wouldn't do to be with my Zawl Tling." So, the cat agreed to take him to Zawl Tling. "Hold on tightly to my tail and do not ever let go." The cat was right; the journey was long and dangerous. They had to cross many swift rivers and climb many cliffs, but eventually, the two made it back to the Underworld, completely unharmed.

When the two lovers saw each other again, they embraced, kissed, and wept like never before. Everything was perfect. There was not a single person who could keep them apart! The couple lived peacefully in the Underworld for some time.

One day, Zawl Tling told Ngan Bawm that there was a vicious bear eating their food from the field. "Let's go and kill the bear," suggested Zawl Tling. So, the couple invited a few of their friends to kill the bear with them. Ngan Bawm and the hunters stood in position, stealthily in the tall grasses.

Suddenly, two red caterpillars with bear-like features (in Chin, *mithi vomkhuai*) appeared in front of Ngan Bawm. "These caterpillars will bite me!" he cried. He hit the caterpillars with his slingshot and killed them.

"Ngan Bawm has killed the vicious bears!" they cheered and danced around in ectasy. Ngan Bawm looked around but he saw no bear. Obviouslforny confused, Ngan Bawm laughed. "What are you talking about? That wasn't a bear." His friends looked back at him, just as confused as he was.

"Are you all crazy or something?" he joked. "But you just killed two bears with your slingshot!" they argued. Ngan Bawm did not really understand what was going on but he knew something was off.

The next day, Zawl Tling told Ngan Bawm to go fishing with the villagers. He, along with some other friends, went to the river to catch some fish. They used *hru* (a special liqiuid from certain trees that caused fish to grow dazed and faint if consumed) to catch the fish.

They were only at the river for a short time, but without warning, dozens of bamboo leaves began to sprout out of the water. "Wow! Look at them all! I've never seen this much fish before!" the dead people all laughed and tried to catch the slippery fish. Ngan Bawm caught some, too, but he was very confused.

These weren't fish, they were bamboo leaves. He couldn't bring home bamboo leaves, because they were useless to eat. So, he threw them away. He left one big leaf in his little straw basket, hoping Zawl Tling would have an explanation for this.

When he returned home, Zawl Tling happily grabbed the bamboo leaf and started to cook it. "What a nice fish you caught, my love!" she praised him. Ngan Bawm shook his head. "But that's not a fish! It's a bamboo leaf!" he protested. Zawl Tling pondered about why her lover saw something other than what she and the rest of the dead people saw.

Finally, she understood. It was because Ngan Bawm was not officially dead yet. He hadn't died; therefore, he could not see things the way the rest of them did. Zawl Tling went to him and explained what he needed to do. "My love, go back to the upper world, where everyone is still living, and carry out these instructions," she said.

"Buy yourself two chickens. Eat one of them with pepper and tomatoes, and let the other one live. Attach a *tahtlem* (a sharp instrument used for weaving on looms) on the ceiling and allow the chicken to step on it. Underneath the ceiling, spread a leather sheet and lie on it, facing upwards." Ngan Bawm bid his love farewell and journeyed back to the living.

There, he did as Zawl Tling instructed and bought the two chickens, ate one, and carried out the rest of her instructions. He lay down on the leather sheet, facing upwards. The living chicken climbed up to the ceiling and stepped on the *tahtlem*, causing it to plunge towards Ngan Bawm, killing him.

Ngan Bawm died and his body returned to the Underworld, where he was happily greeted by Zawl Tling and all his friends. He could see things the way they did now. The bears, the fish, the people, everything.

The couple lived in the Underworld for a while, but soon grew tired of it. They decided to become *Ṭekbu ruang* (a type of branch that holds a fruit called *ṭekbu*). The couple transformed into the branch, and since they were husband and wife, their branches intertwined with each other. When the people saw them, they were really quite surprised, for normal *ṭekbu* branches did not look like that.

"This is not a real *Ṭekbu* ruang," they said. So, they cut them and burned them in a fire. From the ashes of the fire, a vast lake was formed. Zawl Tling and Ngan Bawm were reborn as fish in the lake. They always followed each other and never once were they divided.

Soon, however, they were caught and cooked in another fire. In the process, their eyes popped off and floated into the sky.

Legend has it that they floated into the heavens where they turned into planets (stars). Zawl Tling turned into Venus and Ngan Bawm turned into Jupiter. They were separated! Venus and Jupiter only meet once a year, when the Earth completes one full revolution. When they were living, they were forbidden to be together, and even after death, the curse lingered.